Mitchell's Professional Library

Quality on Site

Ian Ferguson MA (Cantab), MSc, Dip Arch, ARIAS
Eric Mitchell HND, ACIOB, MIMBM

B T Batsford Limited   London

Drawings by Jean Marshall

First published 1986

Printed and bound in
Great Britain by
Anchor Brendon Ltd
Tiptree, Essex
Published by B T Batsford Ltd
4 Fitzhardinge Street, London W1H 0AH

British Library Cataloguing in Publication Data

Ferguson, Ian
    Quality on site.—(Mitchell's professional library)
    1. Building sites—Management
    I. Title   II. Mitchell, Eric   III. Series
    624'.068   TH438
ISBN 0 7134 4666 8

.

Contents

Introduction

The quality achieved on site depends upon many factors, but the principal ones may be identified as follows:
- poor communication of design intention
- design difficult to build
- poor quality labour
- poor quality supervision
- complex and ineffective contract documentation
- unrealistic constraints of time and cost
- historical reasons: separation of design and construction.

Communications in the construction industry were reviewed in the Tavistock Report of 1965[1] and have been the subject of constant debate since. Little has happened, however, other than the relaxing of the Code of Conduct for architects, now allowing them to act as developers. This has forced many of them to consider the implications of their design intentions for the building process.

Designs may be admirable, but may still be difficult to build. Considerable research has been carried out both into design rationalisation and into the production process. In particular significant work has been carried out by the Building Research Establishment in England and Wales[2] and by the Scottish Development Department and National Building Agency in Scotland illustrating that savings of between 25–30% in site labour costs are possible if designs are rationalised[3]. Rationalisation can improve quality on site by smoothing the production process, thereby making it easier to organise, but inherently difficult features must still be eliminated, since the result may be bodging or the taking of 'short cuts' by the builder, with an inevitable loss of quality.

Poor quality labour is a feature of modern building practice. If the labour cannot work at the required level of quality for a particular job, it is unsuitable. Reasons for poor quality labour include much reduced periods of apprenticeship, the result in turn of high wages and emphasis upon speed, the replacement of much trade working by automation, poor recruitment of quality labour owing to the uncertainty of employment in the industry and the tendency of the tradesmen to be promoted to technocratic and managerial positions.

Poor quality supervision is one of the most significant features affecting quality on sites. If supervisors are badly trained and paid and poorly motivated, labour will become demotivated and work will suffer. The site agent in particular has often been regarded as little better than a senior tradesman, rather than as the manager of a significant production process. Things are now improving, with the better training of site managers and the introduction of distance-learning packages by the Construction Industry Training Board. Building Research Establishment research[4] has identified the need for good relations on site between the site manager and the Clerk of Works if quality is to be maintained, owing to the atmosphere of co-operation this can create. Effective support from head office is also essential, plus good working conditions and the according of proper status to site management.

Complex and ineffective contract documentation: the contract documents are often designed to guard against exploitation of the parties to a contract by each other, but good will and a mutual desire to see the job done is the only effective contract principle. Complication can create suspicion through misunderstanding and confusion. Problems of covering all eventualities, of defining clearly what is required, and of allowing for changes in costs and time-scales are reinforced by the different objectives of client, designer and builder. Problems can be caused by sub-contractors, especially where nominated, and by differing design and professional inputs, such as those from services and structural engineers and from cost consultants. All such features can obscure the underlying objectives of all parties, which are to get the job built quickly, at the right quality levels and with a reasonable return to everybody involved.

Unrealistic constraints of time and cost: if a design must be built quickly, quality may suffer, unless an appropriate contracting system has been selected and a design has been made which is quick to build. Fast building may be relatively more expensive, however, unless the returns to the client, once the building is complete, offset high construction costs, with a relatively rapid pay-back. Conversely, where the pay-back is insignificant, construction rates may be slowed. Enough time should always be allowed to build a scheme and the choice of contractor should reflect the desire to build within a certain time-scale at the agreed quality level. An accurate assessment of initial versus life cycle costs, covering durability and maintenance, must be made to ensure that the client can select the appropriate trade-off between the two. Initial design and construction periods must be balanced in the same way with the expected life of the building and the durability of its different parts.

Finally, underlying these factors, quality on site depends upon a much better integration between and understanding of the design and building processes. The historical reasons for the separation between the two stretch back to the beginning of the nineteenth century and to the formation of the professional institutes.[5] Once architecture, in particular, began to be seen as predominantly one of the creative arts, alongside painting, sculpture and music, it became distanced from the craft of building. This in turn led to creative 'movements' and 'isms', which turned architecture from sound building into a branch of fashion, often comprehensible only to the experts. This in turn led to the decay of craftsmanship, since designers knew less and therefore cared less about the art of building and neglected their responsibilities in this area. Once craftsmanship had decayed and, worse, had become the property of the building organisation, it began to be constrained largely by motives of profit, with the results referred to above.

Summary
Quality on site can be achieved only if the many factors contributing to sound building make it possible. These begin with the brief, which describes the client's requirements and the limitations of time and money which he wishes to impose, proceed through the design process and arrive finally at the man on the job by way of the contractor's organisation. This book will discuss aspects of this sequence before setting out in detail some of the ways in which quality on site can be improved by careful attention from members of the design and building teams.

References
[1]Tavistock Institute, *Communications in the Building Industry*, 1965
[2]Forbes/Stjernstedt, *The Finchampstead Project*, Current Paper CP 23/72, BRE, 1972
[3]NBA/Scottish Development Department, *The Cottages Report* : Report No. 665, HMSO, 1978
[4]Bentley, M J C, *Quality Control on Building Sites*, Current Paper CP 7/81, BRE, 1981
[5]Saint, Andrew, *The Image of the Architect*, Yale University Press, 1983

1 The brief

The quality achieved by the man on the job, assembling the building in the factory or on site, depends ultimately upon the quality of brief produced by the client or building owner.

The brief should include some description of required quality levels, which must be understood and interpreted by the designer. It is convenient to describe quality in terms of four major factors, each supported and reinforced by the constraints of time and cost.

Factors
(a) Purpose
(b) Functional performance
(c) Appearance
(d) Experience

} Time and cost

(a) Purpose

The building's purpose must be clearly defined: what is the building for? Once it is built, how long is it likely to have this purpose? For example, will major additions be likely within a few years of completion? Should the design therefore be flexible and indeterminate? Purpose will have a major effect upon quality levels: a prestige building will be built to a higher level of quality than a utilitarian one; conversely, it would be a misuse of resources to design and build a utilitarian building to standards that were too exacting. Furthermore, available resources must be used and directed in ways appropriate to a building's function: low cost housing should be durable and capable of sustaining low levels of maintenance; a prestige office building on the other hand, in addition to having a relatively short life and being maintained at a high level, may require heavy expenditure on the executive suite, but less upon the general office. Other factors affecting purpose include phasing of the construction, this being related to available finance, whether different parts of the building are likely to be changed equally frequently and the likely costs of change. Ease of change in terms of time required to make it is another factor.

(b) Functional performance

Functional performance is decided in terms of the finance available and of the technical and spatial qualities required. Financial considerations include construction costs, professional fees, interest on loans and, once the building is built, rates of return on renting or leasing, amortisation of capital and allowances on depreciation and maintenance. Usually, design and construction phases are completed as quickly as possible, to minimise the costs of borrowing, to reduce the effects of inflation and to enable the building to yield a return with the least delay. On the other hand, speed of construction may have to be matched to the finance available, in terms of cash flow and of available capital, for example as when selling new housing units, where resource is generated by rate of sale and profit levels. Since the effect of delay is to tie money up for a longer period than expected, building costs will have to be kept down to compensate, thereby affecting quality levels.

Technical performance can be considered in terms of the spatial arrangement of the building and its performance as a system. The brief describes the accommodation required and gives some idea of how it is to be disposed within the building envelope. If this disposition is made in a random and unsystematic way, for example if there are very few rooms of the same size and if all the staircases are different, each solution becomes a 'one off' and the operative must learn each new job from scratch. This has a fundamental effect upon quality: a highly individualistic building will require higher quality labour, take longer to build and therefore cost more than one where there is a greater degree of repetition. This may be justified, but both client and designer should be aware of the likely consequences.

As a system, the building should perform as required by its purpose and should be designed to integrate the major functions of strength and stability, environmental performance and services. Integration is difficult to achieve and in terms of built quality it requires an understanding by the designer of how different trades work, the time they require to carry out their work and the skill and supervision levels likely to be available. A major factor in the construction of a complex building may be the extensive use of specialist sub-contractors, whose working practices vary and who may need highly skilled supervision to ensure effective control.

The parts of the building likely to have the greatest effects upon perceived quality are the finishes and fittings. These are usually chosen to offer the maximum effect for least expenditure, unless conspicuous expenditure is required. Their construction and fitting should lie within the competence of the operatives available, anything more demanding having a major effect upon cost, since special skills will have to be imported. Where finishes and fittings are likely to be changed during the building's life, it should be possible to do this at reasonable cost and within realistic time scales.

(c) Appearance

A building's appearance is dictated by a number of factors. For the client, these may include image and status, to assist personal or corporate presentation. For the designer, objectives may be governed by various sets of formal ideas, the result of professional training and interest in building design, and by a desire for approval by his or her peer group. The building's users, on the other hand, may be influenced by familiarity and nostalgia or by the association of ideas with certain cultural and symbolic norms. Finally, society may expect the building to 'fit in', to relate well to neighbouring buildings and to correspond to the prevailing visual ethos. Combined, these pressures can result in building forms which are difficult to construct and which prevent useful repetition of elements and sub-assemblies, thereby making it hard to achieve high quality. Where there is sufficient money available this may not matter, since labour of appropriate quality can be afforded. Usually this is not the case, however, and either a compromise is necessary or design must be so skilful that it gives the impression of high quality, even though actual costs are relatively low.

(d) Experience

The 'experience' of the building is the way in which it performs for the occupiers and those in contact with it, such as visitors and passers-by. Convenience in use is of primary importance. Spaces must be the right shape and size for the activities going on in them and should be properly related to each other. Services should be where they are required and the environmental performance of the building must make it comfortable to occupy in all climatic conditions. As with 'appearance' and 'purpose' the client and the designer have the task of creating a building which can be built to the level of quality appropriate to the time and money available, as measured both during the construction phase and during the building's life. After completion, easy maintenance and adequate durability are important factors in satisfying both building owners and users. Thus, maintenance staff may not be able to apply their skills at the right quality levels unless the building encourages maintenance at these levels. For example, choice of floor finishes and skirting details can make floor-cleaning either easy or difficult and, unless maintenance is carried out properly at regular intervals, durability will suffer. Furthermore, when components or sub-assemblies have to be repaired or replaced, it must be possible to carry out this work quickly and economically.

2 Agreed quality levels

Each of the factors affecting quality has to be agreed independently, related to the other factors, and then communicated along the chain of command to the operative on site. At each link in the chain, further inputs may be made, for example by the general and sub-contractors, by the site managers and by the operatives themselves. Also, and crucially at each stage, interpretation of the quality required may both vary and be given greater or lesser importance. This is because each organisation and individual making an input has certain requirements and motivations peculiar to itself. For example, the contractor may want to maximise his profits from the job, the sub-contractor to do only so much work in one particular week, the site manager to work to his interpretation of his firm's standards and the operative to work to the limitations of his particular skills and financial expectations. Quality may also be affected by changes in financial and technical performance as design and building work proceed: the method of financing the job may change or the returns on the completed building may not reach expectations, requiring alterations to be made in design and specification. Alternatively, there may be changes in technical standards or in materials and techniques of assembly: these may have to be introduced if 'mandatory', or be an option if only 'desirable', but in either case there will be the need for a late updating which will affect the agreed quality levels; there must therefore be methods of accommodating change during the design and building processes. These will also be necessary during the life of the building, since flexibility – the ability to accommodate change in use and performance – may not only be a design requirement, but also affect durability and maintenance, which may require the demounting and fitting of new components at quality levels prevailing at some time in the future.

There are three main parties involved in the making of a new building or the refurbishing of an old one: the client, the designer and the builder, although any of these functions may be combined. These parties must agree, before the job starts on site, the quality levels to which they intend to work. The problem they face in doing this is illustrated in *2.01(a)*: the *client* wishes to have a building as near perfect as possible, completed in the shortest possible time and at the lowest possible cost; the *designer* strives for a perfect building and tries to persuade the client to spend sufficiently in order to achieve this; the *builder* on the other hand, wishes to maximise the return on his investment and works to those quality levels which enable him to do so. In addition to the difference in level of quality sought by each party in relation to cost, however, there is a difference in type of quality. For example, the *client* may be interested in the amount of lettable space provided, the *designer* in

14

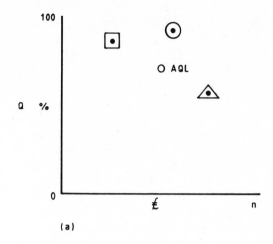

(a)

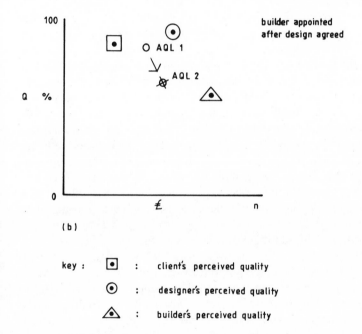

(b)

key :   ▣   :   client's perceived quality

         ⊙   :   designer's perceived quality

         ◬   :   builder's perceived quality

2.01   *Agreed quality levels*

the building's visual and spatial attributes and the *builder* in good buildability, enabling him to get the building built and his money back quickly.

In reality, a compromise has to be reached, and in *2.01(a)* this is indicated by a plain circle, which is the point at which all parties ultimately agree to set the quality for the job. The method of doing this varies with the building procurement system chosen. For example, diagram *2.01(b)*, based on *2.01(a)*, shows how two stages of compromise have to be reached when the builder is not appointed until after the design has been agreed between the client and the designer. The initial agreement reached at AQL 1 may have to be altered to accommodate the input from the builder, resulting in AQL 2.

Having agreed that quality levels for any particular job have to be set in terms both of type and level, the question then arises of how these criteria are to be described and measured. One way to approach a solution is to re-define 'level' as 'amount', where 'amount' corresponds to value for money, measurable by objective standards, 'type' to 'perceived' quality, measurable by subjective ones. It is possible to measure objective standards more precisely than subjective ones, which are therefore the ones which cause the most difficulty. For example, the thermal regime of a building can be designed precisely, but its appearance may result in sharp disagreement between the different parties involved.

Two possible methods of measuring quality levels in terms of 'amount' and 'type' are described in Appendix 1. The first method is to make subjective assessments of the quality levels required for the new building under each heading (purpose, technical performance, appearance, experience) using rating scales of 1–10 or 1–100: this exercise would be carried out by the client, the designer and the builder separately. Once all the parties had made their assessments, results would be compared and a compromise agreed. A similar exercise would be carried out in terms of the building's life-cycle performance, thereby enabling some balance to be struck between initial and long-term factors such as durability and maintenance. As an example of how this might work, local authority housing would be expected to yield relatively low ratings overall for financial and technical performance as new building compared with a prestige office, but achieve good ratings for appearance and experience, since houses are more sensitive to psycho-social factors than offices and are occupied for longer periods of time. In the examples chosen, similar results might appear for life-cycle costs: low-cost housing must continue to be cheap and durable, whilst occupiers may be prepared to spend quite large sums upon maintaining and upgrading offices.

A second method of measuring the AQL of a building is to establish the highest and lowest acceptability quality levels for each of the major parameters, possibly as percentages, and to select from within each range the quality level required. This is an overall figure applied to the building works as a whole. It would then be possible to apply this rating to each building stage and indeed to each trade, omitting those stages where particular quality levels were not relevant. Again, this would initially be a mixture of objective and subjective assessments carried out by each party, with results being compared and compromises reached. Once the building had been completed, the exercise could be repeated in order to compare planned with actual performance. Success would be declared if the achieved AQL 2 *(2.01(b))* approximated to the planned one.

3   Transmitting quality levels

Once agreed quality levels have been established for a new building, they must be transmitted down the chain of command from the client, working with the designer, to the operative on site. This is a hazardous procedure, as has been documented repeatedly within the Industry[1]. The principal reasons for failing to interpret the client's requirements correctly are as follows:

(i)   The client and designer may not agree clearly about the brief for the building's purpose, performance, appearance or experience.

(ii)   The designer's views about level and type of quality may differ from those of the client.

(iii)   The designer may not succeed in interpreting the quality agreement correctly, either because he has misunderstood it or because he does not have the necessary skills.

(iv)   The designer may design a building which cannot be built to the agreed quality levels: there is a misfit between design, buildability and cost.

(v)   There may not be enough money to build to the designed quality levels (or, rarely, there may be too much).

(vi)   There may not be enough time to design or to build to the agreed quality levels.

(vii)   The builder may not understand what the agreed quality levels are: a communications failure.

(viii)   The builder may not be able to build at the agreed quality levels, owing to a misfit between the design and the builder's skills and resources.

(ix)   The design intentions may not be communicated clearly to the building operative.

(x)   There may be a poor balance between initial and life-cycle costs, resulting from a poor brief, making it difficult to maintain the building at the agreed quality levels.

Taking these points in turn:

(i)   The major factors determining the brief and controlling its influence upon quality have been discussed in chapter 1. It will be evident that failure by client and designer to agree the brief clearly will adversely affect both quality and communication, which must be precise to be effective.

(ii)   Designers may either resist the client's instructions, because even after discussion they do not accept them, or be given too much freedom by the client, with the result that a design is produced to which the client objects. In either case, the design intention may become confused and it will be difficult to agree a realistic quality level.

(iii)   Even after discussion, the designer may not fully understand the client's

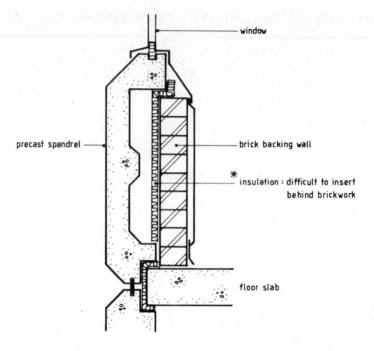

window

precast spandrel

brick backing wall

* insulation : difficult to insert
behind brickwork

floor slab

fitting insulation behind a spandrel panel

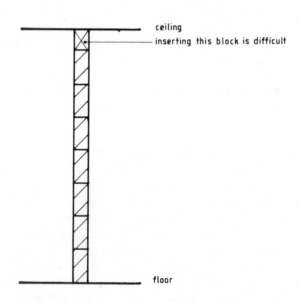

ceiling

inserting this block is difficult

floor

building a wall between floor and ceiling planes

3.01   *Difficult-to-build details*

approach to quality and may 'design in' his own version of quality in the wrong places. Alternatively, given a complex brief, its interpretation may be beyond the skills of the designer. For example, a housing designer may be asked to take on a multi-storey office building. In both cases, quality will suffer and the quality level will be altered. If this occurs late in the job, when the client realises that corrective action is needed, the consequences can be delay and financial loss.

(iv)   A common failure is for designers to design buildings that are either difficult or impossible to build without alteration *(3.01)*. Communication will therefore be ineffective, since the builder will have to alter the design to make construction possible. Apart from resulting in delay, this can cause the client to suffer financially, since the alterations made by the builder will often be to the builder's advantage.

(v)   Quality levels may be established at such a high level that they cannot be afforded. This may result either from a failure to reconcile the financial commitments accurately at the briefing stage, or from the designer misunderstanding the implications of his design proposals for the building process.

(vi)   Unless the client has been quite clear from the outset about when he wants his building, a designer or builder may be chosen who is incapable of delivering the building on time; both design and building processes may be too lengthy. It is important to select the most appropriate communications and procurement procedures for the job in hand.

(vii)   If design is complete before the builder is appointed, there is a risk of choosing a builder who either does not understand the quality levels required or who is unable to deliver them. This can lead to delay whilst the builder is 'educated' and to expense whilst abortive or inaccurate work is corrected and claims are settled.

(viii)   Even if the builder is competent to deliver a building at the right quality levels, he may have misunderstood the information passed to him owing to a failure in communication.

(ix)   Once the builder has received and absorbed the building information at head office, it must be transmitted to site management, to the sub-contractors and to the operatives. This places a heavy responsibility upon building management to ensure both that the information is complete and that it is presented to the site in a form in which it can be assimilated and applied.

(x)   A building may be designed and built which, whilst being satisfactory initially, is found to be too expensive to maintain: it may be too costly to heat and light, inflexibly planned or be made of insufficiently durable materials.

It will be apparent, therefore that achieving quality is very largely to do with communication, between client and designer, between client, designer and builder, and within the building organisation itself. The agreed quality levels must be clearly expressed down the chains of command, in an

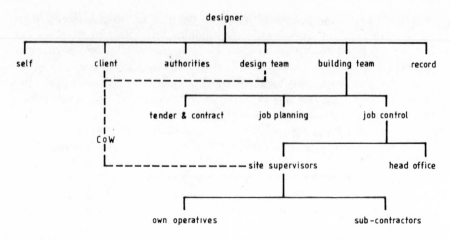

note : most communications are two-way

3.02   *Communications hierarchy*

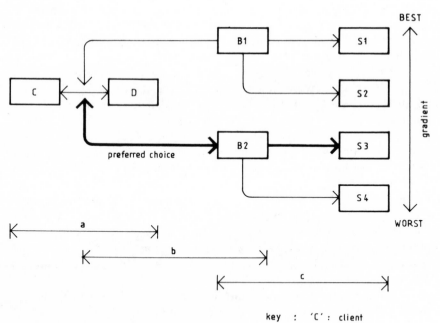

key :   'C' : client
         'D' : designer
         'B' : builder
         'S' : site teams

         a : design stage
         b : contract & tender
         c : building

3.03   *Quality gradient*

20

unambiguous way and in a form related to the needs of each individual and organisation *(3.02)*. Furthermore, there must be opportunities for checking the correctness of instructions and for inputs to be made at each stage in the interest of efficiency and progress. The procedure is illustrated in *3.03*. Client and designer agree the brief and fix their joint quality level for the job. A builder is then selected with experience in this kind of work and capable of building at the agreed quality level. (The builder may be selected earlier and be able to make some contribution to design decision-making.) The builder transmits the agreed quality level (AQL 2 in *2.01(b)*) to a site team capable of building at the appropriate quality level. Thus, in the diagram, 'S1' represents the team belonging to the best builder capable of working to the highest standards and therefore at the top of the 'quality gradient' whilst 'S4' represents the team working at the lowest acceptable standard. The team chosen may fall somewhere between these extremes, its choice governed by availability and price in addition to the ability to satisfy the quality standards for the job.

Having agreed the quality levels for the job and appointed the builder, the next task is to select the appropriate documentation for transmitting these levels.

Reference
[1]Tavistock Institute, *Communications in the Building Industry*, 1965.

4 Documentation

'Quality' instructions are transmitted from the client to the designer and down the chain to command to the operative using various systems of documentation[1]. Usually, these consist of drawings, specifications, cost control documents (Bills and Schedules) and verbal instructions; during the progress of the building works, additional instructions may be produced in the form of drawings, variation orders (architect's instructions) notes, letters, etc. The form of documentation is related to the type of instruction being transmitted and to the recipient of the instruction. For example, information about the spatial arrangement and form of a building is transmitted by drawing or diagram, whilst that about quality is communicated mainly in writing, by reference to existing standards and practices.

The type of drawing and written description will vary with the originator and the recipient of the instruction. A *client* is probably unskilled in drawing and will communicate his intentions in writing or verbally. The *designer* can usually communicate most easily by drawing or diagram, the *builder* best verbally or with simple sketches and the *operative* by demonstrating, using tools, materials and craft techniques. Effective communication must also be in the forms which are most easily assimilated by the intended recipients. For example, a drawing intended to inform the client what his proposed building will look like is not much help to the operative who has to build it from day to day; a set of written quality references intended to satisfy the building control officer will not help the builder to order exactly the right materials for the quality levels agreed.

Documentation is required for different purposes during the course of the job. These purposes vary from agreeing the brief to, for instance, establishing where the wall ties should be placed and how they should be fixed. The range of documentation required and the means used to communicate can be listed as follows:

	Primary	**Secondary**
(a) **Instruction from client to designer**	Rough sketch	Written and verbal description
(b) **Initial design proposals**	Sketch drawing	Written descriptions of quality standards
(c) **Local authority approvals**	Outline production drawings	Written descriptions and references
(d) **Tender and contract**	General production drawings	Written descriptions and references

| (e) **Building (main contractor)** | General and detail production drawings | Written descriptions and references |
| (f) **Building (operatives)** | Trade specific drawings | Written descriptions and verbal instructions |

It will be noticed from this list that, as the 'quality' instructions pass down the communications hierarchy, they have to change both in form and content. For example, whereas the contractor's head office may be happy with a set of general and detail production drawings, the site agent may find that he has to translate these drawings into forms which are meaningful to the sub-contractors and tradesmen.

Considering the list in more detail:

(a) Client/designer

The individual client's rough sketch may give no more than a two-dimensional outline of the building required, with only a broad indication of accommodation and technical performance. These tentative ideas are then expanded in meetings with the designer to include verbal and written descriptions. The corporate client, on the other hand, can be expected to produce a substantial document conveying not only the anticipated purpose of the building but also detailed information about the financial and technical performance required from it. The absorption and analysis of the information contained in this document may be a considerable undertaking in itself, requiring a number of meetings and discussions before the client's intentions are fully grasped.

(b) Initial design proposals

The designer makes initial proposals for the building using drawings, models and brief descriptions of the quality standards proposed. These drawings have two principal functions: to convey to the client that the brief has been understood and to persuade him to accept the designer's interpretation of the brief – in effect, to serve as a marketing exercise. The drawings are therefore very largely concerned with the anticipated appearance and experience of the building. The written descriptions of the outline quality standards proposed may, where they are concerned with technical performance, be quite specific, for example in proposing aluminium windows or a 'high-tech' roof structure, but the implications of these standards for buildability, cost and time have yet to be worked out. For this reason, there is a serious risk at this early stage that the client will be asked to accept design proposals that are impractical, or which cannot be realised for the money available without compromising important parts of the brief. He may also be asked to commit himself to a building where the life cycle costs are either hard to predict or likely to be high, because new materials or assembly techniques are proposed which have not been properly tested, or because components and sub-assemblies are being asked to perform in ways which will threaten durability.

It is essential, therefore, that at this early stage quality levels are agreed which are physically achievable and which can be contained within the budget proposed both initially and for the life of the building: the documentation should not be designed to deceive the client and, where innovation is thought necessary, it should be supported by appropriate research and by evidence that the proposed solution is a practical one. For example, low cost housing may rarely justify technically advanced solutions, since both initial and life cycle costs must be low, the building must be durable and the users may be unskilled in maintenance procedures; the same may be true, broadly, of schools. On the other hand, prestige commercial buildings may justify advanced technical solutions, since the client may be relatively insensitive to initial and life cycle costs and since the building's image may override other considerations. Its life, too, may be short compared with housing.

(c) Local Authorities' approvals

The documentation required for obtaining planning and building regulation approvals[2] consists of drawings, supported by written descriptions and references to relevant Codes and Standards. The drawings will be those agreed with the client as representing the required building accurately; cost studies will have been completed and by this stage the design will have been finalised in all major respects. The information required by the Authorities will relate to the technical performance and appearance of the building and must be presented in a way which enables them to extract the information which they require. The form of presentation, whilst developed from that used to 'sell' the scheme to the client, will not have a marketing function, unless lay comment is required. As with the sketch designs, however, there is a risk that design commitments will be made that are difficult to realise in practice, unless the implications for cost, time and the building process have been fully understood by both client and designer.

(d) Tender and contract

Once approvals have been obtained, documentation is prepared for tender and contract purposes. This requires drawings, written descriptions and references completed in sufficient detail and in such a form that builders can understand fully what is required and submit realistic prices for the work. To do this, they must be told what the building's purpose is, what its appearance will be and the level of technical performance required. This is a critical stage in the transmission of agreed quality levels down the communications hierarchy (3.02): up to this point, a process of discussion between client and designer has resulted in the fixing of AQL 1 (2.01(a)); it is now a matter of arriving at AQL 2 (2.01(b)). It is necessary therefore to select a builder who is capable of building the scheme to the quality levels agreed by the client and designer (3.03). To do this, it will be necessary to follow a procedure such as one of those described in Appendix 1 and to fix for each part of the work and for the project overall the quality standards required, measured in terms of level and type.

The documentation prepared for tender, and subsequently for contract purposes, must include information capable of being interpreted and applied

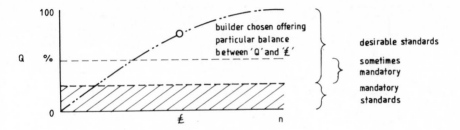

4.01   *Relationship between quality and cost*

by the builders selected, if the failures discussed previously are not to occur. For example, all builders must be capable of meeting the fixed standards for the building, that is those required by regulation and concerned with such matters as fire and structural stability. It is usually desirable for all builders to meet standards which, although not mandatory, are those needed to satisfy sound building practice. However, not all builders need to be capable of meeting the highest possible standards of technical performance. Often a '50%' building will be satisfactory and is perhaps all that the client wants or can afford. This point is made in *4.01*. It can be seen that, for any particular job, a builder should be chosen from within the zone of 'desirable standards', balancing the choice between tender price and the quality level required. The aim of the designer must be to choose materials, components and sub-assemblies which are capable of being assembled into the building with just that level of skill from the builder which will minimise construction cost and time. It follows that the documentation at this stage must be sufficient in type and amount to produce accurate tenders from builders capable of working to the quality levels described. For example, for complex, high quality schemes, it may be possible to define quality standards in terms of indicative drawings and performance specifications in which the builders likely to tender are left free to make their own proposals for carrying out the work. On the other hand, for simpler schemes, likely to attract the less capable builder, it may be necessary to provide a full and detailed description of the work. In either case it will be apparent how much easier the agreeing of AQL 2 and the preparation of an accurate price will be if the builder is involved in the design process from an early stage and can contribute his practical thinking as the pre-contract stages progress.

(e) Building stage: the contractor's needs
Once the builder has been selected, full production information is passed to him to enable him to build the building[3]. Unless he has been involved in the design process from an early stage, this is the first opportunity he will have had to assess the full implications of what he has successfully tendered for. The tasks required of the builder at this stage mean that a great deal has to be done in the short time between being awarded the contract and going on site. The drawings, written descriptions and references must therefore be such as to assist him in understanding the design and in ordering materials and

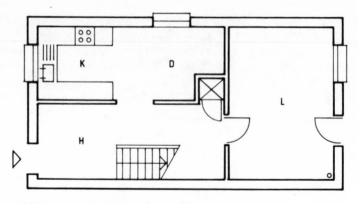

general arrangement, for tender, contract and job control

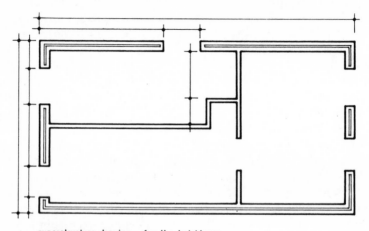

superstructure drawing, for the bricklayer

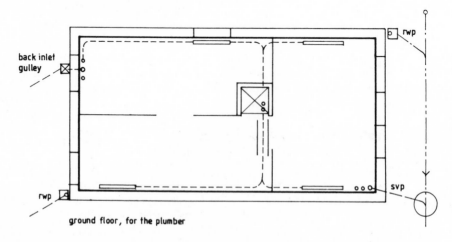

ground floor, for the plumber

4.02 *Drawings for different purposes/stages of work*

components as quickly as possible. For example, if a drawing contains information affecting the work of several different trades, these must be separated out like strands in a rope to see what the work content of each is *(4.02)*; it is also necessary to examine the interfaces between trades, to assess likely interference and the consequent need for a higher level of management input. It is worth noting that the defining of standards by reference to lists of Codes of Practice and British Standards can waste a great deal of time. The Institute of Building has identified the problems caused on sites by the inexplicit use of British Standard Codes of Practice and Specifications[4]. Few builders possess full sets of these, especially of Codes, which are expensive to buy and often inaccessible for quick reference. Designers and contract management must therefore describe clearly what is required, at least where unusual references are made. Other problems are that the language of the Code may be difficult to understand and that it may not be clear which of the several quality levels or methods of working contained within the Standard are to be used. Designers should remember that it is on the basis of the drawings, written descriptions and references that the builder makes key management decisions, such as what skill level of site manager to appoint and which sub-contractors to choose. The documentation, in relation to the contract period, will also be the basis for the programme, which is the key in turn to job financing and to the ordering and delivery of plant, materials and components. The requirements for production documentation can be summarised as follows:

Building purpose
General arrangement drawings, not fully detailed
Technical performance
Key drawings of the whole building
Detailed drawings of each part, related to the key drawings
Schedules of components related to the key and detailed drawings
Written descriptions and references, covering:
    manufactured components and sub-assemblies
    Codes and Standards
    Cost factors
    Time factors
    Special contract conditions.

(f) Building stage: the operatives' needs[5,6]

Information is passed from the builder's head office to the site team capable of working at the agreed quality levels *(3.03)*. The site manager or agent is the recipient of this information and has the primary responsibility for interpreting it and transmitting it to the operatives. In doing this, he may be assisted by a Clerk of Works, and by the trades foremen. To enable him to build the building, the site manager must have the following documentation:

Drawings
Bore hole details; information about previous works on the site

Block plans of the scheme
Site, services and drainage layouts
Key drawings, including plans, elevations and sections
Detail drawings for foundations, walls, floors and roofs
Structural details
Mechanical and electrical services details
Joinery details for both standard and special features
Lintel, door, window, ironmongery and colour schedules
External works details

Specifications
Written descriptions and references to quality standards (avoiding simple
    listings of Codes and BSS references)

Bills of Quantities
Listing materials, components and work required in terms of quantity and
    price and defining any special contract conditions

Orders
Copies of orders already placed by head office
Method of placing orders: for materials, components, sub-contractors and
    plant

Programme
Programme of work in bar chart, line of balance or network form

Statutory documents
Accident book, registers of inspection for excavations, scaffolds, lifting gear,
    etc
Building Regulation approvals and notification cards.

To be effective, however, the site manager must be aware of the quality
standards to which he is expected to work. These will be defined partly by the
documents above, in terms of the building's purpose, technical performance
and appearance, and partly by the accepted standards in the firm itself: these
standards will be agreed with senior management in a set of specific criteria,
but equally important, will be part of the 'atmosphere' of the firm. This in
turn will be created by such factors as fair payment and bonusing systems,
good on-site facilities for operatives, well-maintained plant and safe
scaffolding. The attention given to such items will set the standards for the
site and consequently for the quality of work.

Having assimilated the documentation himself, the site agent must pass
relevant information on to the operatives. His methods of doing this will vary.
For example:

Meetings can be held and information transmitted verbally; on larger
contracts it is especially important to hold regular meetings with trades
foremen at which to review progress, plan future work, check availability and
need for labour, materials and plant, pass on instructions and information and

generally to ensure that trades are working effectively together.

Mock-ups and sample panels can be built

Drawings can be made of difficult details.

Where trades foremen are working principally as managers on site, they will pass on instructions verbally to the operatives for whom they are responsible. Occasionally, they may have to set out the work themselves, for example where this is difficult or when newly trained labour is being used. On smaller jobs, tradesmen will be instructed direct and issued with any necessary drawings and information, some of which might be pre-recorded on tape suitable for use in portable cassette players.

In addition to selecting the right methods for transmitting quality instructions initially, quality control must be exercised over the period of the contract. This will be done on a day to day basis by the trades foremen, site agent and clerk of works, on a weekly basis by the contracts manager or job architect and on an occasional and random basis by senior management and principal consultants. There will also be specialised supervision of sub-contractors, especially where their work is unusual or difficult. Ultimately, the quality on site is controlled by the man on the job. If he is not properly trained or motivated, quality levels will fall, regardless of supervision. Research published in 1981 by the Building Research Establishment[7] identified two main sources of failure in site quality: failure to do the work properly and failure in documentation. The first of these, it was discovered, was a function of the efficiency of site supervision. For example, if there was a strained relationship between the site manager and the Clerk of Works, quality would suffer, since supervision would be less systematic and rigorous and there would be less willingness by each party to help the other out. Failure in documentation was found to be common and relatively hard to remedy. If drawings were incorrect or inadequate, work would be wrongly built or delay caused. Both caused frustration and affected performance.

Two other factors requiring specialised documentation and the sensitive transmission of information are worth special mention. These are:
- the use of sub-contractors
- changes in design during the course of the work.

Drawings and instructions issued to sub-contractors may have to be more specific or different in emphasis from those required for a firm's own men. This is because a sub-contractor may have his own method of working and be differently motivated, expecting to work to his own standards of quality and over shorter or longer time scales than the remainder of the work-force. This may call for different types of drawings and instructions, and regular meetings to explain the conventions in use by the general contractor and designer on that particular job.

Finally, changes in design during the course of the job can disrupt working patterns and sequences and de-motivate both supervisors and operatives. For example, where, on a weekly visit, a designer condemns a piece of brickwork,

29

his instruction may be that the work has to be rebuilt. The work may indeed be unsatisfactory and apparent as such to all; it may, on the other hand, be the result of poor communication at the beginning of the job of the quality standard likely to be acceptable, or less forgivably, of a change in mind about either the design or the standard. Whatever the reason, a lack of clarity about design intention and of acceptable quality standards can create annoyance and frustration, thereby risking not only poor performance, but also increased costs and delays in completion. It is essential, therefore, for procedures for dealing with changes in design to be established at the beginning of the Contract, for changes to be instructed in writing and for all variations in the work to be dealt with by the builder in a systematic manner which does not 'raise the temperature' of the site.

References

[1]RIBA, *Plan of work for design team operation*, RIBA Publications London

[2]BRE, *Project information for statutory authorities*, Digest No. 271, HMSO

[3]BRE, *Working drawings*, Digest No. 172, HMSO

[4]Woolven, D R, *How is quality determined on site?* (article) 'Building Technology & Management' 3/8

[5]Site Management Section, Information Services, No. 38, *Information requirements for site operatives,* Institute of Building, 1971

[6]National House-building Council, *Registered house-builders' site manual*, NHBC

[7]Bentley, M J C, *Quality Control on Building Sites*, Current Paper CP 7/81, BRE, 1981

5 Organising the production process

(a) The head office team

Once the contract is let and it has been agreed to proceed with building, the contractor must begin to organise the production process[1]. The immediate problem he faces is shortage of time. Especially if a lump sum contract has been let, apart from the tender drawings and documentation and a visit to the site, this may be the first time the contractor has seen the contract and full set of detail drawings. Indeed, the full set of drawings and specifications may even now not be available, regardless of the contract conditions. The result is that the contractor has little time in which to organise the work. Unless he is geared to a quick response and is already familiar with the kind of work to be done, he may find it difficult to complete his preparations by the time work on site is due to start. For this reason, clients and designers must select contractors carefully when drawing up tender lists, basing their choice upon known performance and suitability for the work to be carried out.

To give some idea of the complexity involved, the contractor must carry out the following major activities when organising the production process and before going on site:

(i) Select the management team for the job
(ii) Meet and discuss the job with the client and the design team
(iii) Study and assess the full implications of the drawings, specifications and other production documents
(iv) Select sub-contractors; meet and discuss the job with any nominated sub-contractors and suppliers
(v) Select supervisors and key operatives; ensure sufficient own labour will be available
(vi) Order materials and components, starting with those likely to have long delivery times, such as lifts and manufactured joinery
(vii) Programme the work
(viii) Arrange finance, including loans, guarantees, bonds, etc
(ix) Satisfy himself about certification and cash flow arrangements
(x) Arrange for the availability of plant, tools and equipment
(xi) Agree details of site establishment, including huts, compounds, temporary services, etc, and the obtaining of any planning approvals, road closures, etc, required
(xii) Implement any initial contracts required such as temporary site services, roadworks, drainage and piling.

This is a formidable task for any but the smallest job and one that requires the deployment of considerable management expertise, even given familiarity with the general nature of the work. For example, setting up the management team: do the managers have the necessary experience? Will they be available for the whole job, or only part of it? Will there be enough management input? Will specialist management for any part of the work be necessary, for example over mechanical and engineering teams? Or again, taking programming and scheduling: what kind of programme is most suitable? Is there enough time and labour available to complete the job? If not, what other resources are required and when should they be available? What kind of management system will be necessary to control the job on site and hence the ultimate quality on site?

It will be apparent from this brief description why the late involvement of the contractor in the pre-contract stages can incur the risk of poor quality control. Although the contractor will have assessed his ability to carry out the work when deciding to tender, he will still have to do a great many things during the short period between being awarded the contract and starting work on site, including absorbing unexpected additions to the production drawings and documentation, resolving the position on Provisional Sums and setting up sometimes complex arrangements with sub-contractors and suppliers. Although early involvement will not eliminate these problems, it will assist the contractor by enabling him to plan his resources well ahead and to suggest amendments to design and specification which will make construction quicker and easier. This will be particularly effective where the building is complex.

(b) The site team

Whilst making his internal arrangements at head office, the contractor will be considering who will carry out the work on site and how this work will be organised. To do this, he must consider many of the points referred to in (a). For example, which site managers will be available with the necessary experience for the work? How much support will be required from line management? Will specialist on-site management be necessary at certain stages? Which of the firm's own men will be allocated to the job? How many sub-contractors will be on site at any one time? Will there be a clerk of works; if not, who will be the client's representative both on and off site?

The selection and motivation of the site team is complex and crucially important to the ultimate success of the project. Heading the team is the site manager who, apart from being technically competent, must have the personal qualities and motivation to enable him to control his labour force, progress the job and to 'get on' both with those superior to him and with the least experienced apprentice. Quality on site depends ultimately upon the quality of the men carrying out the work. The key to achieving this quality is the site manager.

Diagram 5.01 illustrates the organisation of the site team. In many contracting organisations, however, the number of operatives actually employed by the firm may be minimal, often confined to labourers and to a few specialist trades, such as machine operators, bricklayers and joiners. The rest of the work will be carried out by sub-contractors and their presence

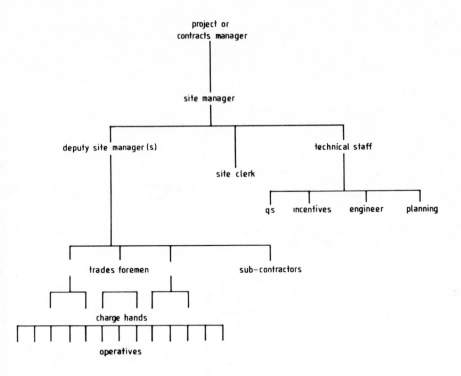

numbers of staff actually resident on site will be dictated by the complexity and size of the project

5.01 *Organisation of the site team*

creates a major problem for site management; for although sub-contractors may be well known to the firm and be used regularly, almost as though they were the firm's own employees, they may also be new and untried, either for commercial reasons – their prices at tender were lower – or because they will be engaged on specialist work. In both cases they will be obedient to their internal management systems and to their own motivations and rules. The problem is illustrated diagrammatically in *5.02*. The existence on site of men working to different sets of rules and motivations can have a disruptive effect upon the regular labour force, usually because of different attitudes to time and money.

Apart from the organisation of the site team, certain key decisions must be made affecting the building process itself, for example, concreting and mortar; should these be mixed on site or supplied ready-mixed, in which case a method of checking delivered quality must be agreed with the designer? Or again, how should bulk materials and major components be handled? Will full mechanical handling be used? Will deliveries be palleted? Will protective covers be fixed by suppliers or must sheeting and storage under cover be provided on site? In what order should deliveries be made: block by block or floor by floor? Or again, decisions will be required about temporary works, that is those works which enable building work to proceed smoothly and safely: for example, what type of scaffolding will be most suitable? Can

33

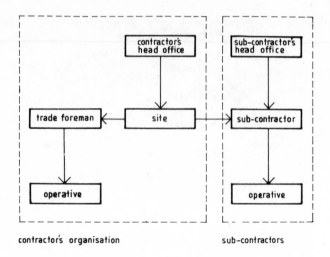

contractor's organisation   sub-contractors

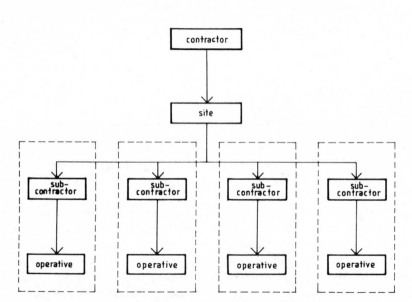

several sub-contractors

5.02 *Managing sub-contractors*

formwork be made up on site or will it be necessary to use proprietary systems? How will the excavated spoil be disposed of and where can retained spoil be stored? Will temporary accesses and roads be necessary and where can they be routed?

(c) Financial factors

The National Joint Council for the Building Industry, Working Rule Agreements (WRA), set out the agreements made nationally between employers' and operatives' representatives in the industry. These fix the wage rates and determine the conditions of employment for operatives, reinforced sometimes by clauses in contracts which supply further guidelines on rates of pay, hours and conditions of work. Health and safety on site are controlled and regulated for by the Construction Regulations (1961 and 1966)[2] and by the Health and Safety at Work Act (1974)[3]. Quality on site can be affected markedly by operatives' attitudes to pay and conditions which, regardless of national agreements, can be surprising. For example, there is within the workforce a substantial nomadic element which sees short term employment as positively desirable and which is less interested in working conditions than in good, flat rates of pay. Forms of payment can be complex, varying from standard hourly rates to rates with additional elements such as incentive schemes, travelling expenses, tool allowances and compensation for difficult working conditions. There may also be responsibility money, sickness and injury benefits, holiday allowances and retirement benefit schemes. Finally, lump sums may be paid to operatives who pay their own taxes and insurances.

For men to be properly motivated to work to the right quality levels, they must be treated fairly. Disgruntled labour will skimp work and will leave the job when better work comes along. Fair treatment includes working conditions, now largely protected by legislation and by the Trades Unions, and fair method and size of financial reward. Basic wages may be agreed within the industry but disagreements often start when discussing 'bonusing' and extra payment for specialist and difficult work. The basis for employment must be clearly agreed with the labour force, the agreement adhered to and payment made regularly. Only when this is done can the labour force be expected to respond and to work loyally to achieve the firm's objectives. The factors affecting operatives' skills and motivations are illustrated in *5.03*.

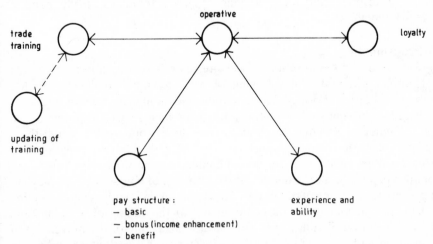

5.03   *Skills and motivations of the operative*

(d) Labour quality

Quality on site is governed by the quality of the men actually doing the work, however good the management, working conditions and pay. In recent years, there have been radical changes in the quality of operatives, often for the worse. The main reasons for this are:

(i) The shortening of apprenticeships, leading to lower levels of knowledge and practical skill
(ii) The replacement of many craft and manual skills by automated processes
(iii) The fixing of quality levels for components and assemblies at the minimum levels tolerated by standards and regulations
(iv) Fewer skilled men and women presenting themselves for training in the industry, owing to uncertainty about employment prospects
(v) Still primitive working conditions and limited financial reward
(vi) The promotion of the better quality workers to technical and managerial jobs, thereby removing them from the site.

Given poor quality in the labour force, management, and in turn the designer, are forced to simplify the building process to bring it within the competence of the operatives; this degrading simply reinforces the decay in craft skills however. Method of payment can have a further detrimental effect whenever it encourages speed at the expense of quality, and can have a fundamental influence upon the level of craft skill available.

Finally the presence on site of a varying and sometimes large population of sub-contractors can cause havoc with carefully agreed wage and bonusing systems. Sub-contractors will work to their own norms, according to agreements reached with the general contractor's management. In practice, this may lead to erratic working hours and to financial returns which will differ sharply sometimes from those of the firm's own operatives. This can have a powerful de-motivating influence, unless carefully and firmly handled by management.

(e) Programming

The selection and organisation of the site team is related intimately to the programme for the job[2]. Slow moving jobs can accommodate delays, whether caused by materials shortages or by inefficiencies at management or operative levels. Fast moving and complex jobs, with many specialist inputs, will require higher level management and better quality operatives. Under these circumstances, the manager must be familiar with different programming systems, for example bar chart, line of balance and network, and how to use them to keep the job on schedule. Programming, of course, extends beyond simple day to day control of labour to the ordering, scheduling and accepting of deliveries of materials and components, to the calling off of plant and equipment (and to its return to store), to the arranging of the movement of materials in and out of store and their transfer to the work place and to the testing and commissioning of completed pieces of work.

To exercise this detailed control, management must often devise tender and contract programmes, in addition to the short term or stage ones. The tender programme may be required during estimating to enable the method and timing of the construction process to be worked out and to assess accurately requirements for labour, plant and any temporary works. For example, it is essential to know as early as possible the sequencing of key operations and how they should be fitted together efficiently to ensure the smooth running of the job. The main purpose of the contract programme, on the other hand, is to enable contracts' and site management to decide the sequence of construction, dates and times for the ordering and delivery of materials and components and to fix latest times for the receipt of information and the initiating of sub-contracts. This programme requires more detailed information about labour and plant requirements than does the tender programme.

References
[1]Pilcher, R, *Principles of Construction Management* (2nd edition), McGraw-Hill
[2]*Construction Regulations 1961 and 1966*
[3]*Health and Safety at Work Act, 1974*

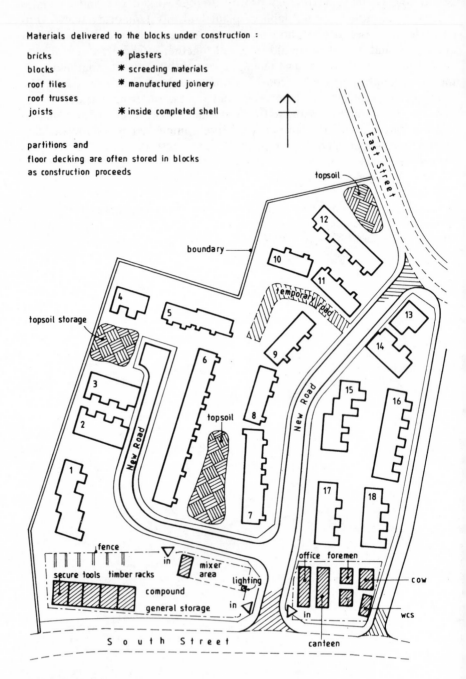

Materials delivered to the blocks under construction :

bricks   * plasters
blocks   * screeding materials
roof tiles   * manufactured joinery
roof trusses
joists   * inside completed shell

partitions and
floor decking are often stored in blocks
as construction proceeds

6.01 *Typical housing site: Compound and soil storage*

6   The building process

(a) General

Once pre-start planning is complete, work moves to the site. The site team has been chosen and the site manager has spent time at head office going through the drawings and documents and in familiarising himself with the job. With his aid, the project planner has drawn up the job programmes, the buyer has arranged supply of both bulk materials and specialist items, plant and equipment have been commissioned, advance work necessary to establish site services has been completed, and, most important, the lines of communication between head office and site have been clearly established: quality on site depends fundamentally upon a clear system of communication.

(b) Establishing the site

On Day 1, the first task is to establish the site, setting up the site huts, compound and any satellite storage areas. The next step is to fence the compound area itself, make temporary drainage and service connections and establish routes for deliveries of materials both to the compound and to the places of work. The location of compound and job control centre may be of great importance in controlling the efficiency of the job (6.01): they should normally be located centrally, to minimise travel distance between place of work and storage and rest areas. This requirement may be modified, however, by the need for ease of access by delivery vehicles and for phasing, which may in any case require the moving of the compound and site offices later in the job. On cramped urban sites, the compound may occupy an area which will be built on later and the site offices may have to be re-located, sometimes outside the site boundary.

(c) Materials and components

Quality on site is greatly dependent upon the safe arrival at the work-place of undamaged materials and components. To this end, it may be necessary to provide temporary access roads, or at least to ensure that the permanent roads have been laid to base course level to allow vehicles delivering breakable items, such as drainage goods, to get close to the work-place. A further reason for this arrangement is to reduce the risk of theft: if materials such as bricks and blocks are off-loaded alongside the main access roads, it is probable that they will be subject to damage, theft or vandalism. There is less chance of this if they are stored either within the site or, better still, within the site compound. Temporary access roads may be required in any case if heavy plant will be required for assembly purposes. Off-loading and storage of materials, if managed carelessly, can result in their being badly damaged or unusable. Before it became common practice to band, sheet and pallet bricks

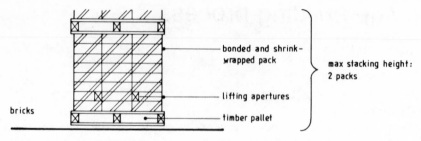

bricks

stack on hard-standing or on timbers, clear of
ground

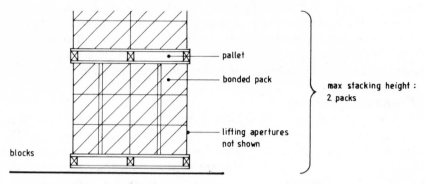

blocks

protect from weather and splashing by passing site
traffic : use sheeting if packs not shrink-wrapped

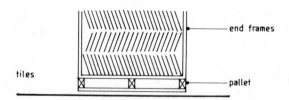

tiles

6.02 *Storage of bricks, blocks, tiles on site*

and blocks, for example, bricks could be damaged by being tipped from the
vehicle. Although this practice has largely ceased, brick and block packs may
still be off-loaded onto soft ground, where they will sink into the mud and
make it impossible to use the bottom rows of bricks in the pack; worse,
operatives may try to use them when they have become saturated, dirty and
possibly exposed to frost action. It is important, therefore, that these
components are fully sheeted before delivery and protected afterwards *(6.02)*
(6.05). Timber components are also seriously at risk from mis-handling. In
particular, roof trusses are likely to be damaged by incorrect off-loading[1],
followed by incorrect storage, although all joinery items, including floor
joists, windows, door sets and timber lengths, can be rendered useless by bad

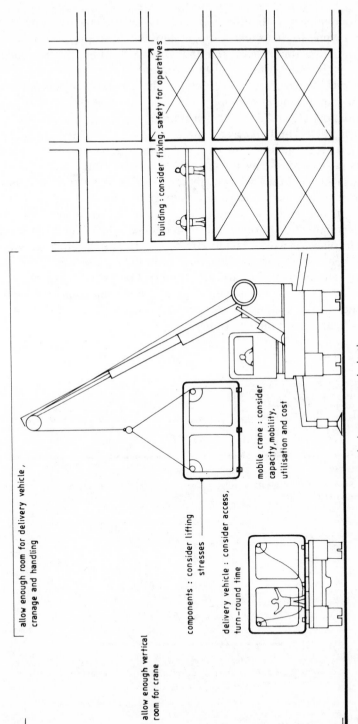

allow enough room for delivery vehicle, cranage and handling

allow enough vertical room for crane

components : consider lifting stresses

delivery vehicle : consider access, turn-round time

mobile crane : consider capacity, mobility, utilisation and cost

ground : bearing capacity, level

building : consider fixing, safety for operatives

6.03 *Off-loading directly onto the building*

41

treatment[2]. Damage is most serious in three areas: actual physical damage resulting from impact with other objects, movement and twisting in the component owing to incorrect storage and the absorption of excessive moisture from the atmosphere and the ground, leading to the fixing of components with unduly high moisture contents. This can be a ·problem, particularly with timber frame construction. The risk of damage is minimised by off-loading and fixing in one operation.

This is both possible and desirable with certain types of frame construction, for example light steel and precast concrete, and with cladding and infill panel systems *(6.03)*. It is in any case financially undesirable to have high cost components in storage on site for any length of time; rather, their delivery should be delayed until they are actually required for fixing into the building. This also reduces the risk of accidental damage and theft.

Damage can occur at any stage. For example, an avoidable risk is the incorrect handling of materials and components across site from storage compound to place of work. This particularly affects such items as window frames, finished joinery components, board and sheet materials[3,4], especially plasterboards and lightweight partitions, and certain plumbing items such as sanitary fittings[5]. The risk is made much greater if unsuitable plant is used for handling, such as the ubiquitous dumper and excavator, and if there are no level access roads round the site *(6.04)*.

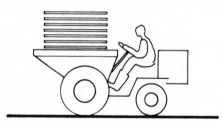

INCORRECT method of carrying plasterboards across site

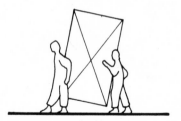

MANHANDLE plasterboard sheets vertically

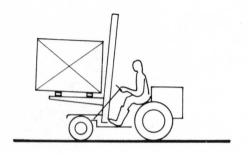

CORRECT method of carrying sheeted packs across site using the fork–lift

6.04 *Handling materials on site*

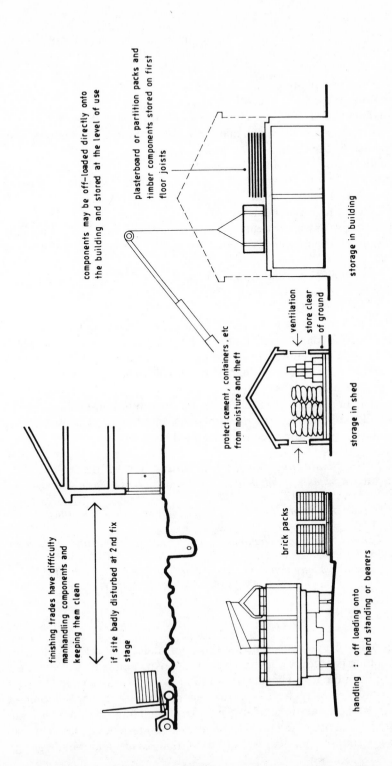

components may be off-loaded directly onto
the building and stored at the level of use

plasterboard or partition packs and
timber components stored on first
floor joists

storage in building

ventilation
store clear
of ground

protect cement, containers, etc
from moisture and theft

storage in shed

finishing trades have difficulty
manhandling components and
keeping them clean

if site badly disturbed at 2nd fix
stage

brick packs

handling : off loading onto
hard standing or bearers

6.05 Handling and storing materials and components

43

Solutions include:

Delaying delivery until the components are needed, when the risks of damage from vandalism can be minimised

Minimising handling by:

- off-loading and fixing in one operation
- off-loading adjacent to the work-place
- off-loading and storing in a completed part of the building *(6.05)*
- delivering in job packs, which may be organised in terms of building size, stage size or floor size
- off-loading onto a suitable *hard standing*
- proper *protection* of components against accidental damage, moisture and splashing by site traffic
- protection of high risk items by using special stores
- proper *storage* of timber items to prevent straining, twisting and warping
- provision of clean and level *accesses to the work-place* for delivery vehicles
- *site transit handling* using suitable vehicles, with easily damaged items delivered directly to the work-place.

That insufficient attention is given to the protection of materials and components against damage is emphasised by the extensive wastage which can occur during and after delivery, amounting to as much as 100% more than has been allowed during estimating[6]. It is difficult to achieve quality on site where such a situation exists.

Finally, it is important to ensure that the operative himself handles the materials and components correctly, applying the right type and level of skill and using the proper and correctly maintained tools for the job.

References

[1]BRE/DoE, *Pitched roofs : trussed rafters – site storage* : DAS 5, BRE

[2]BRE/DoE, *Wood windows and door frames : care on site during storage and installation*, DAS 11, BRE

[3]BRE/DoE, *Suspended timber floors : chipboard flooring – storage and installation*, DAS 32, BRE

[4]TRADA, *Care of timber and wood-based sheet materials on building sites*, Wood Information Sheet 4–12, TRADA

[5]BRE/DoE, *Plastics sanitary pipework : storage and handling*, DAS 40, BRE

[6]BRE, *Waste of building materials*, Digest No. 247, BRE/HMSO

(d) Stages of work

(i) Setting out[7] Key levels and setting out points, together with the decision-making procedure for this stage of the work, must be agreed at the very beginning of the job. The quality of the job can be badly affected by poor setting out, which may be a difficult operation on sites with complex contouring or where there are a large number of buildings each of which has to be related to the other and to a system of roads and services. Designers can do much to simplify matters by ensuring that roads and buildings are geometrically related to each other and can be set out using the skills and surveying equipment likely to be available. This may be especially important on complex housing sites, with many small units set at odd angles to each other (6.06), or on sites where there are existing buildings to which the new ones must be related.

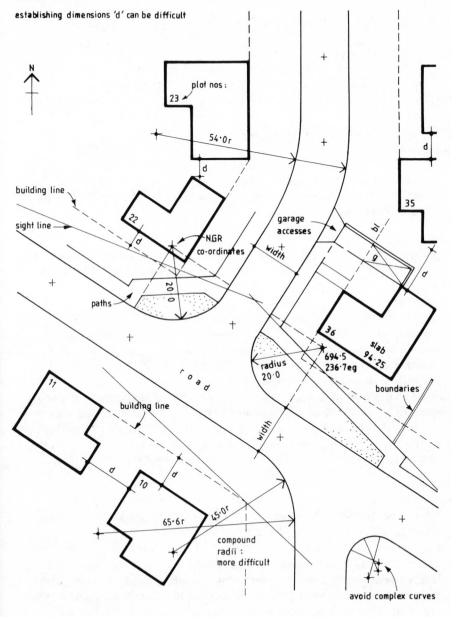

establishing dimensions 'd' can be difficult

N

plot nos :

23

54·0r

d

building line

sight line

22

NGR
co-ordinates

garage
accesses

width

35

bl

g

d

paths

20·0

36

slab
94·25

694·5
236·7eg

radius
20·0

road

boundaries

11

building line

d

d

10

width

65·6r

45·0r

compound
radii :
more difficult

avoid complex curves

drains and services must be added
ALSO levels and datums

6.06 *Setting out the site*

Factors to take into account include:

Complexity of layout

Numbers and types of building and whether new or existing

Road layouts

Both new and existing; their relationship to new and existing buildings

Services and drainage[8]

Statutory Boards will have preferred routes for main services: how will these affect road and building layouts?

Distribution systems: will these be under footpaths, roads or grassed and landscaped areas?

Sub-stations: location and size

Streetlighting

Drainage and manholes: will systems be separate or combined? Are the locations of the outfall sewers known?

(Note that the layout of the drainage system must be integrated with the road and building layouts.)

Landscape features

It is essential to plot accurately the locations of trees, existing planted areas, walls, fences, etc, where these form boundaries or are to be retained

Poor ground [9,10]

Identification must be made of soft spots, water courses, high water tables, running sand, 'made' ground, old basements, mine workings, etc

Certain areas may have to be avoided or require special treatment, for example where there is chemical pollution or disturbed ground requiring excavation and consolidation

It should be noted that, especially on urban sites, it is common to discover areas of poor or unbuildable ground which were not located on survey or when trial holes were dug. This may require new design and specification of the roads, services and building layouts. In any case, remeasurement will be necessary.

Phasing

Stage completion may affect setting out, especially where design changes for later stages are likely to occur (as with private housing sites). For example, temporary boundaries may have to be established

Survey and measuring equipment[11]: In addition to simple sight rails, tapes, string lines and builder's squares, equipment may include theodolites and levels of various types. It is important to have available skills able to operate the equipment being used, such as line and level engineers and surveyors

Careful supervision of this work by trades foremen, site agents and Clerks of Works is vital and equipment must be stored under cover, protected from damage and theft and regularly maintained to ensure accuracy.

References
[7]BRE, *Setting out sites*, Digests 202, 234, HMSO
[8]British Gas, *Gas in housing*, British Gas
[9]BRE, *Fill* : Pt 2 – *Site investigations*, Digest No. 275, HMSO
[10]CIRIA/PSA, *Site investigation manual*
[11]Hewitt, *Guide to Site Surveying*, Architectural Press

(ii) Site clearance and reducing levels   As a result of design and survey, it will have been decided which areas are to be built on and what levels are to be worked to. Unbuilt-on areas of the site will be left clear of building for future hard-standing, landscape features and possible new building or extensions. Other areas must be left free for the stockpiling of topsoil; these should not be so far away that carting becomes an expensive operation *(6.01)*

Summary of factors to take into account:
Site clearance
On urban and re-development sites, ensure existing services have been located and diverted where necessary
If Statutory Board drawings do not show routes accruately, it may be necessary to use cable detectors, etc, to establish routes
Clear identification of trees and other features which are to be retained must be made. *Note*, in this respect, that plant operators should be given clear instructions to avoid damage to trees, fences and other features.
It is important to preserve the quality of topsoil by controlling the depth of dig
Stockpiling of topsoil: location and size of tips must be decided
Avoid excessive plant movement over areas of poor ground

Labour
Ensure availability of skilled labour related to the plant being used and to the tasks being carried out; provide clear instructions and training where necessary; provide adequate supervision of the work

Plant and equipment
Ensure properly maintained plant is available and that it is related to the job in hand: tracked excavator, bulldozer, tractor with back acter, roller and specialised plant may be needed
Blade and bucket size and type must be decided. Depth of excavation will dictate length of the dipper arm on the excavators and type of ground the power necessary, and whether tracked or tyred vehicles are most suitable. Limited working areas will affect slew angles, heights and general mobility

Reducing levels
Ensure accurate marking of levels; profiles and pegs should be visible and not easily distrubed
Carting and storing of soil should be minimised; decide upon the size and type of lorries used for cartage. Lorry routes should be cleaned regularly when on tarmaced surfaces
Where areas of building are to be hardcored as levels are reduced, ensure supplies are available

(iii) Roads and services Trenching and excavation for roads and underground services can greatly affect ease of movement around the site. Unless this work is completed early in the programme, it will be difficult or impossible for delivery vehicles to reach the areas where building is taking place, leading to the problems of storage, theft and double-handling already referred to. If the trenching for service mains and drainage is left until the building shells are complete, and especially if the weather at that stage is bad, chaos can afflict the finishing trades, who must handle fragile materials across mud and excavation and bring dirt and damp into the building interiors *(6.05)*. It is especially important to ensure that the Statutory Boards co-operate in this respect.

Factors to take into account include:

Roads, drainage and services layout
See 'Setting Out' for general points
Road design should allow for access to buildings by delivery vehicles, otherwise temporary roads or double-handling may be required
Foundations, drainage and services trenches may interfere with each other, both in line and level and in depth of dig
Drainage and services should either be under roads, with pick-up points clearly marked, or be routed through areas which are not critical in relation to building operations.

Road design and construction.[12]
Consider design standards, contract arrangements, width and depth of construction, reinforcement, kerbing and drainage
Location of sewers and services: it may be possible to provide ducts under roads where future requirements are known
Partial completion of roads to base course level, leaving the laying of the wearing course to a later stage, allows access for delivery vehicles
Width of access roads should be suitable for large vehicles
Footpaths and car parking areas may be left until later stages of the contract.

Drains and sewers
Early completion of sewers is highly desirable; this work is often completed as part of the roadworks contract
Phasing of building drain connections should be considered
When laying drains, consider depth of trenching, shoring and planking, bedding, laying and connecting, first testing, back-filling and second testing; locate man-holes and rodding eyes correctly.

Services
Consider water, gas, electricity, telephones and cable TV requirements; allow for streetlighting and lighting of public areas
Consider trenching and laying and back-filling
Liaise with the Statutory Boards to agree phasing of installations and the provision of supplies for the testing of building services later in the job.

Note that service mains are often routed through 'adopted' areas and that future access to these mains by the Boards is important.

Labour

Consider skill levels in relation to tools, plant and equipment being used.

Note that the use of sub-contractors for this type of work is common and that integration with the contractor's own labour must be considered by management.

Plant and equipment

Consider the type of plant and whether it is to be hired or to be provided by sub-contractors.

References

[12]DoE/Road Research Laboratory, *Road Note 29* (3rd edition), HMSO 1970 et seq

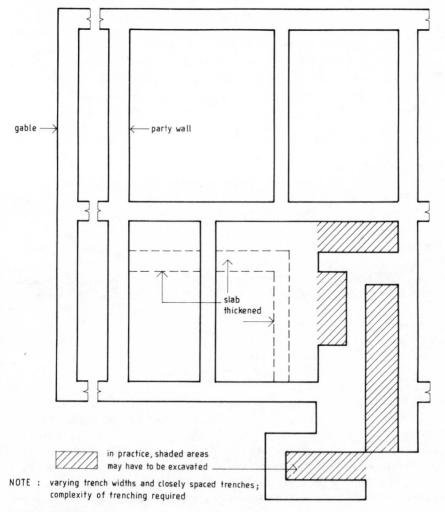

gable →   ← party wall

slab
thickened

⟍⟍⟍⟍ in practice, shaded areas
may have to be excavated

NOTE : varying trench widths and closely spaced trenches;
complexity of trenching required

6.07 *Varying trench widths and closely spaced trenches*

(iv) Substructures: excavation Building work proper begins with excavation of the foundation trenches, unless specialised foundations are being provided, such as deep basements and shear walls, piles or rafts. In most cases, plant is used for excavation, with final levelling and clearing of soil being carried out manually. Design has a major impact upon quality levels at this stage: for example, varying trench widths require different bucket sizes on the excavator, unless the contractor is tempted to save money by double, over or under-digging. Every effort should be made to avoid this, however, since the foundations will not be in accordance with specification. Again, foundations spaced too closely are difficult to excavate, since the weight of the machine can collapse the sides of the trenches *(6.07)*. Also there is nowhere to store the excavated soil except close to the trench, from where it is probable that soil will be knocked back into the trenches, affecting levels and contaminating newly poured concrete. If the contractor is tempted to vary the position and size of excavation to avoid these problems, foundations may be eccentrically loaded or be too shallow. When planking and strutting is required to retain the sides of trenches[13], this must be adequate to protect operatives working in the trenches and a proper cost allowance must be made for this item in the Bills. Trenches must be guarded, to stop people falling in, and great care must be taken to obviate the risk of striking live services during excavation.

Factors to take into account include:

Type of foundation[14,15]
Consider whether to use strip, raft, dry construction, piled, etc, and what the
   implications will be for plant and labour
Ensure that trench width, depth and spacing are correct and that excavation
   can be carried out safely without damaging the trench
Consider whether planking, shoring and strutting are necessary for safety
Consider position of drains and services
Take account of possible underground obstructions, soft spots, running sand,
   etc, leading to the need for back-filling, extra excavation and de-watering.

References
[13]TRADA, *Timber in excavations*, IBL 55, TRADA 1981
[14]BRE, *Soils and foundations* (Pts. 1–3) : Digests 240, 241, 242, HMSO
[15]Barnbrook, G, *House foundations for the builder and building designer*, C & CA

(v) Substructures: concreting foundations[16,17] With simple foundations such as strip, trench fill and pad, mass concrete only will be used. This will occasionally be batch-mixed on site, centrally or adjacent to the work, or, much more likely, be supplied ready-mixed by truck, in which case access must be allowed. With more complex foundations, such as rafts, special mixes and reinforcement will be required, together with the use of formwork. Note also that complications may be caused by changes in level and daywork joints *(6.08)*.
Quality depends upon particular attention to the following[18]:

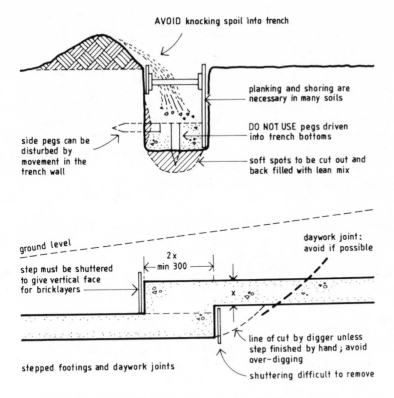

AVOID knocking spoil into trench

planking and shoring are necessary in many soils

DO NOT USE pegs driven into trench bottoms

side pegs can be disturbed by movement in the trench wall

soft spots to be cut out and back filled with lean mix

ground level

daywork joint: avoid if possible

step must be shuttered to give vertical face for bricklayers

2 x min 300

line of cut by digger unless step finished by hand ; avoid over-digging

stepped footings and daywork joints

shuttering difficult to remove

6.08   *Concreting Foundations: problem areas*

Concrete mix
Should be to correct grade and strength for the conditions, including special
  mixes such as sulphate-resisting, and admixtures.

Placing concrete
Consolidation, levelling and finishing: level pegs and markers can move
  owing to movement in the trench walls; timber pegs should not be driven
  into trench bottoms *(6.08)*
Fix formwork accurately and support properly
Reinforcement: fix correctly and use vibrator to compact
Ensure trenches are reasonably dry
Avoid contamination of concrete with earth and rubbish; earth may be
  knocked back into the excavation where spoil is placed too close to the
  trench lip *(6.08)*
Ensure pours are relatively continuous, to prevent concrete 'going-off'
  between deliveries
Where day-work joints are unavoidable, ensure they are made correctly
  (6.08)
Ensure level of top of concrete is accurate, especially with trench fill where
  there are column bases
Cover to assist curing.

Labour

Ensure adequate skill levels are available, especially for controlling mix and placing and for fixing reinforcement.

Note that skilled labour may be required to fix formwork.

Plant and equipment

Ensure vibrators are available when concrete and reinforcement are being placed and that they are used correctly and properly maintained

Allow access for ready-mix trucks

Consider the use of plasticisers to assist with pouring from one location and of conveyors and pumps where reach is a problem

Ensure mixers and pumps are cleaned regularly.

Other factors

Provide clean and protected storage for aggregates and cement *(6.05)*

Minimise site transit handling of mixed concrete

Do not pour below +2°C ambient

Test by cube and slump where necessary[19], and always where reinforcement is being used, ie where concrete is structural.

References

[16]NHBC, *Registered house-builders' foundations manual*, NHBC
[17]Blackledge, G F, *Man on the job* (MoJ) leaflets, Nos 1–18, C & CA
[18]Cement and Concrete Association, *Concrete practice*, C & CA
[19]Blackledge, G F, *The concrete cube test*, C & CA

(vi) Substructures: concreting ground floors   Two types of concrete ground floor construction are common: in situ and precast. The former is usual where the ground is capable of supporting the weight of the slab and of the imposed loads without deflection and cracking. Where weak areas occur, or where point loads are anticipated, the slab must be thickened or reinforced or both. With both in situ and precast work, it may be necessary to consider the provision of ducts and services below the slab, requiring special care in laying pipes and cables and in the consolidation of the sub-base, hardcore and blinding.

Cast concrete slabs   Usually cast upon a damp-proof membrane[21,22], upon a level base of sand blinding, properly supported by well crushed hardcore or hoggin, levelled, rolled and compacted. The same points apply as for concreting foundations: mix, placing, consolidation, reinforcement, levelling and curing are all critical operations. Pours should be continuous and any daywork joints properly made where they can not be avoided[23]. Levelling and finishing are especially important with in situ slabs: levelling requires the use of an accurate perimeter datum, which may be the top of the substructure brickwork or some levelling mark. Finishing varies, depending upon the surface treatment required. For example, screeding must be done late in the job, thereby introducing wet work into the building and restricting entry while it dries. On the other hand, the rough tamped finish is less sensitive to damage during the following stages of construction. Power floating must be carried out at the right time following casting of the slab, which can be difficult in bad weather, when temporary protection may be needed for operatives carrying out this work. For this reason, it is best restricted to work inside a roofed building. Both this process and early grinding leave the surface of the slab vulnerable to damage during shell erection, which may result in the need for filling compound prior to laying the floor finish.

Precast slabs   These are used where it is not possible to depend upon the bearing qualities of the ground, for example where there is a substantial amount of fill, or where quick completion of a working floor surface is required[24,25]. It is essential to select the appropriate span/depth ratios and to ensure there is a level bearing at each end of the slab or plank. It is also necessary to make proper provision for both horizontal and vertical service distribution *(6.09)*. Crane handling is necessary, which implies a risk of damage to components unless care is taken by both crane operator and

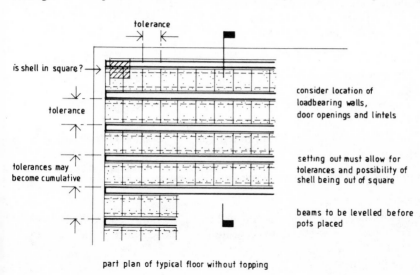

6.09   *Precast beam and pot floors*

banksman. Work should be programmed to minimise storage, by enabling units to be lifted and placed direct from the delivery vehicle. With many systems, an in situ topping to the units is required, sometimes even reinforcement where spans and loadings are considerable. It may be possible to programme this work for later in the job and to pour several bays or even floors together.

In summary, the following quality factors should be considered:

In situ slabs
Preparation
Consider possible needs for ducts, drains and services below the slab; consolidate carefully
Provide sufficient depth of hardcore and blinding, eliminating soft spots before laying, rolling and compacting
Lay and lap sheet dpms, taking care not to tear
Place any reinforcement correctly
Allow sufficient lap to tie in with dpcs.

Mix and placing
See many of the points in (v)
Levelling is especially important, as is the need to fix datums
Concrete should be poured in continuous operations, bay by bay, and bay sizes should be limited to reduce shrinkage
Consider finish: tamped and scabbled for screeding; power floating; early grinding.

Labour, plant and equipment   See (v).

Other factors   See (v).
Expansion joints and designed construction joints may be necessary
Ordering of concrete should be accurate to minimise waste; concrete delivery should be continuous
Areas of saturated ground must be de-watered to prevent the washing out of fines, with consequent lowering of strength.

Precast units
Preparation
Consider provision of ducts and services below floor level.

Type
Consider the type most suitable for the conditions: wide slab, beam and pot infill, prestressed plank, since the placing, handling and finishing of each will be different.

Placing
Crane handling is necessary: can the crane be used for other jobs on site, or is this a sub-contract item, with the sub-contractor providing his own plant?
Care in handling is essential

54

Whenever possible, units should be off-loaded and placed in one operation
Reinforcement and in situ topping may be necessary
Can several toppings be poured at once?
How will the in situ material be handled?

Labour
If sub-contract labour is used, extra organisational and management
   problems may be created
Skill is required by both crane operator and banksman.

Plant and equipment
A crane of appropriate capacity will be needed:
Can it get close to the building and will it have the required reach with the
   largest unit likely to be handled?
If permanent roads have not been laid, is there a temporary access to the
   building for heavy plant?
Concrete mixing and lifting: it may be necessary to pump or skip hoist mixed
   concrete to higher floors; cranage may be needed for lifting screeding and
   other materials later in the job.

Other points
The installation of services in precast floors can be difficult where there is no
   suspended ceiling or sandwich floor for horizontal distribution; vertical
   drops through the floor should be designed in *(6.09)*.

References

[20]Deacon, C, *Concrete ground floors : their design, construction and finish*, C & CA
[21]BRE/DoE, *Substructure : DPCs & DPMs – installation*, DAS 36, BRE
[22]Barnbrook, G, *Concrete ground floor construction for the man on site* : Pts 1 & 2, C
   & CA
[23]Turton, C D, *Plastic cracking of concrete*, C & CA
[24]National House-building Council, Registered house-builders' site manual, NHBC
[25]Dore, E, *Suspended concrete ground floors for housing*, C & CA

(vii) Superstructures: masonry: brick/blockwork Brick and block cavity
construction is the commonest type of construction for low-rise, short-span
building[26–28]. It is less commonly used for infill, non-loadbearing panelling in
framed buildings. Accuracy of setting out and of building are vital, since all
following trades will be constrained by the tolerances established. For
example, plasterboard jointing widths will be affected by the accuracy of the
completed shell. Accuracy of setting out masonry infill is not so important in
framed buildings, since the frames and panels control tolerances. Labour
should be chosen to match the agreed quality level for the building and the
type and stage of work reached.

   Designers should recognise the high costs of complex walling, for example
where there are many corners, stopped ends, etc *(6.10)* and of the extra care
needed to handle and lay certain types of bricks and blocks. For example,
engineering and calcium silicate bricks present quite different problems in

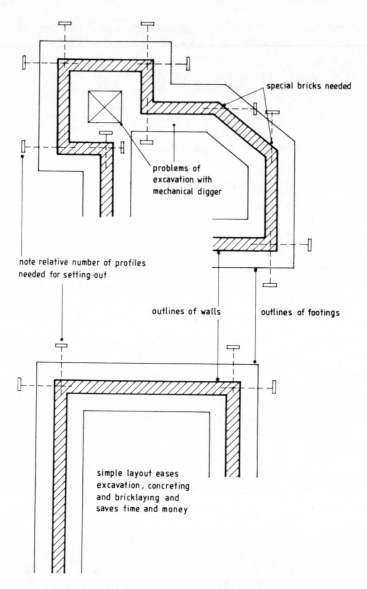

special bricks needed

problems of
excavation with
mechanical digger

note relative number of profiles
needed for setting·out

outlines of walls   outlines of footings

simple layout eases
excavation, concreting
and bricklaying and
saves time and money

6.10 *Foundations and masonry walls: complexity/simplicity*

laying, rustic bricks with contrasting mortar can lead to dirty finished work,
and over-large blocks may be physically difficult to handle.

Mortar specification can have a major effect upon the quality of finished
work[29,30]. If it is of the wrong consistency, it can be difficult to use; too plastic
and it can be squeezed out of joints as the wall settles, disrupting tolerances,
especially at window heads where lintel heights and levels are critical. Mortar
consistency should not vary during the course of the work. If it does, it raises
the problems of controlling the mix, batching and delivery at the work-place.
It may be better for this reason to use pre-mixed mortar with retarding agent,

especially where control of colour is important.

Building in wall-ties[31] and cavity batts[32] for insulation can create problems: ties can end up sloping backwards towards the inner leaf unless location is properly planned and allowance for bed settlement is made. Cavities must also be kept clean to prevent mortar snots resting on the ties and cavity trays. Cavity batts must be properly secured by special ties before the outer leaf is

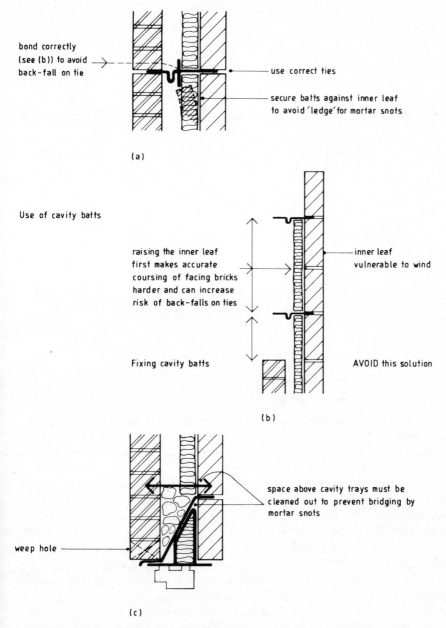

6.11 *Problems with wide cavity construction*

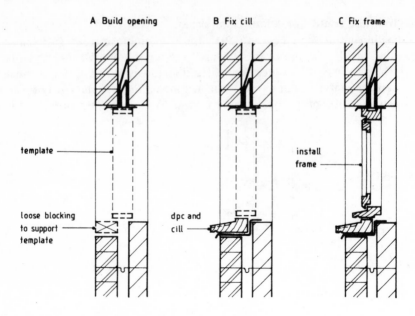

A Build opening   B Fix cill   C Fix frame

template

install frame

loose blocking
to support
template

dpc and
cill

sequence of installation of cill and frame

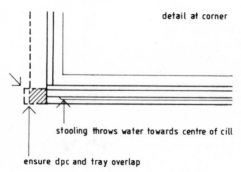

detail at corner

stooling throws water towards centre of cill

ensure dpc and tray overlap

6.12 *Windows: fixing cills and frames*

raised, to prevent the edges of the batts projecting into the cavity, where they can catch mortar snots and allow moisture to reach the inner leaf *(6.11)*. If necessary, blocks should be omitted at the bottoms of walls over cavity trays to allow trays to be cleared of mortar.

Dpcs and lintels: Problems occur when building in vertical dpcs at openings, in ensuring that they are not bridged at the cavity closer and are tucked into the groove in the back of the frame. Attaching vertical dpcs to horizontal dpcs at sills and lintels should be done with care *(6.12)*. Cavity trays should be placed correctly and related to brick and block courses and flashings. *Lintels*: accuracy of levelling, bearing and bedding is essential, but allowance should be made for possible settlement over openings; the handling and placing of large lintels can be difficult.

Floor joists are built into the internal leaves of cavity walls or are seated upon shoes or hangers, which are built in by the bricklayer as the work proceeds[33]. Joists must have a full bearing and be packed and levelled in relation both to each other and to the height of the room below; this may entail the use of cut blocks or coursing bricks to obtain the designed dimension. Where built in, joist ends should be treated against rot and, where seated upon hangers, they should be a tight fit in the hangers, which in turn must be built solidly into the wall. Other points when building joists in are the desirability of spacing them at block dimensions, design permitting, to avoid having to cut blocks, and of leaving space above each joist to allow vertical adjustment during levelling (6.13).

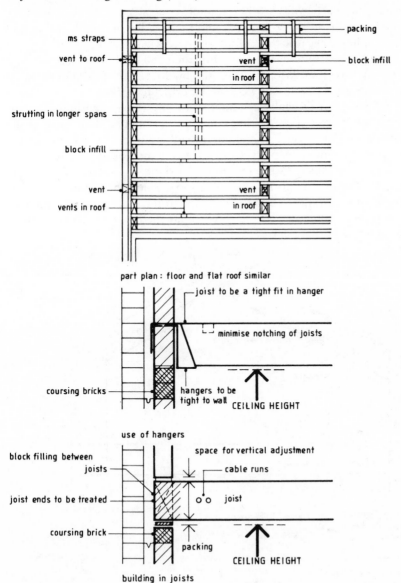

6.13   *Floor joists: quality factors*

Work at eaves and gables: at the eaves, the cavity is normally closed with a row of blocks laid as flat and level as possible to provide a true bedding for the wall plate. This is set in mortar and tied into the blockwork inner leaf with galvanised metal straps. The gable brickwork can either be cut accurately by hand to rake or cut roughly, where it is to be concealed by a bargeboard. The former is a time-consuming process and one requiring considerable skill. Where bargeboards are being provided, slots for gable ladders must be built in and it will also be necessary to provide metal straps and ties to secure the roof trusses.

Separating and party walls must be soundly contructed, with all joints fully bedded and packed with mortar to prevent the passage of sound, smoke and flame. Scaffolding can cause difficulty and where walls in terraces are stepped and staggered, complications are caused by the need to change materials and build in cavity trays and flashings along the line of the roof. Maintenance of upper walls where roofs are stepped can be difficult (6.14).

Partitions can cause difficulty in a number of ways. Load-bearing partitions at ground level in two-storey buildings must be raised at the same time as the external walls, and it is usual to build non-loadbearing partitions at this time too, to avoid bringing the bricklayers back on the job once the shell is complete. This can cause obstructions in the working space, however, making the use of trestles and platforms difficult (6.15). Allowance should be made for drying shrinkage and for tying in securely to the external wall, either by using ties or by building in; note however, that the latter process can affect the block module in the external wall (6.16).

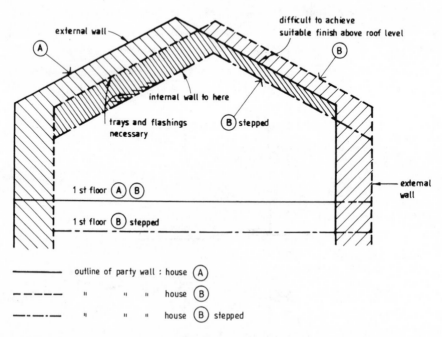

6.14 *Complexity of party walls with stepping/staggering*

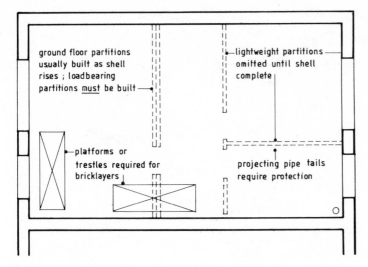

ground floor partitions usually built as shell rises ; loadbearing partitions **must** be built

lightweight partitions omitted until shell complete

platforms or trestles required for bricklayers

projecting pipe tails require protection

6.15   *Partitions omitted to provide working room for bricklayers*

Quality of facing brickwork can be seriously prejudiced by poor detailing, especially round openings and where brickwork is exposed to the weather on both sides, as in parapet and screen walls. Poor choices of bricks and mortar can result in sulphating, effloresence, spalling and the growth of mould on weather faces, especially where walls are heavily insulated. In the British climate, it is essential that water is shed from walls as quickly as possible and to this end copings should be generous, with special attention given to joints between lengths, windows set back in openings, upper walls protected by overhanging eaves and with a full provision of cavity trays, flashings, ventilators and weep-holes. Apart from damage caused by weather, unsightliness can result from poor masking of daywork joints and lifts and by variations in brick colour and mortar specification. Designers can minimise this problem by providing variations in brick detailing at changes in lift, for example by the use of soldier or header courses or slight projections *(6.17)* and by ensuring that where necessary bricks are mixed and that mortar batching is consistent.

Infill panels[34], as has already been mentioned, define their own dimensions and tolerances, being constrained by adjacent panels and by the surrounding frame. They must have room to move, however, since expansion and contraction can cause cracking and detachment of bricks and of brick and tile slips *(6.18)*. This movement will be both between the facing and backing materials and across the face and on long runs it will be necessary to provide movement joints at at least 12 m intervals.

Again, it must be difficult for water to penetrate the facing panel, but having got in it must be impossible for it to get any further; furthermore, it should be possible for water to get out, either by travelling to a weephole or by evaporation to the outside air.

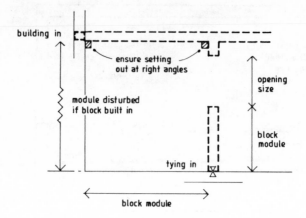

Plan of typical layout

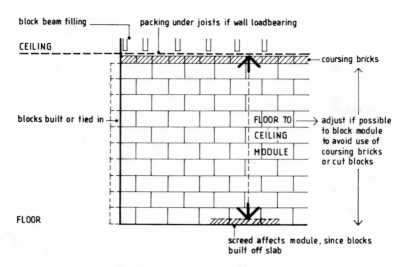

Elevation of typical partition

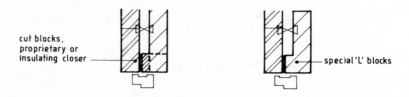

Detail options at closing of cavity

6.16 *Setting out block partitions*

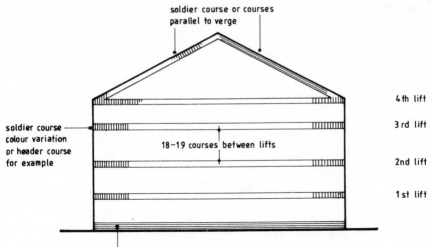

soldier course or courses
parallel to verge

4th lift

3rd lift

soldier course
colour variation
or header course
for example

18–19 courses between lifts

2nd lift

1st lift

change brick colour and / or type for six courses or so , or up to dpc

6.17   *Brick gable walls: techniques to mask lift joints*

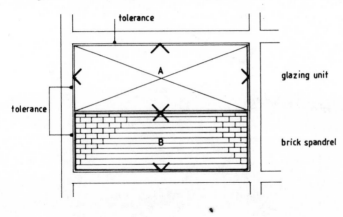

tolerance

A

glazing unit

tolerance

B

brick spandrel

differential movement of frames and panels
A will move differentially from B and from the structural frame

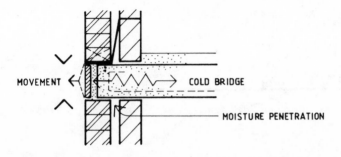

MOVEMENT

COLD BRIDGE

MOISTURE PENETRATION

avoid use of tile slips, especially in this location

6.18   *Framed construction: movement and tolerances*

63

In summary
Setting out
Ensure accuracy and avoid complex design, which will make both setting out
 and construction more difficult.

Tolerances
Consider the relationship between masonry and other trades' tolerances.

Design
Avoid complex detailing and minimise changes in direction on plan of
 masonry walling
Choose correct bricks and mortar for climatic exposure and insulation
 conditions
'Design out' problems caused by building practice, such as lifts and daywork
 joints
Avoid stepping and staggering in terraces and 'lean to' construction *(6.19)*.

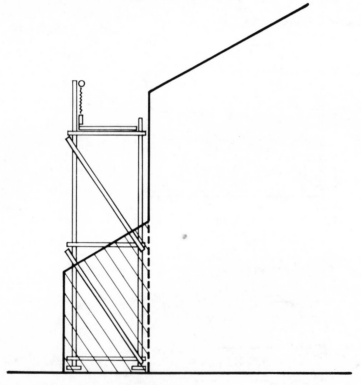

6.19 *'Lean-to' construction and scaffolding*

Cavity walls
Build in cavity batts correctly
Raise leaves in correct order and avoid wall ties sloping back
Provide flashings, trays barriers, etc, and ensure trays are cleaned out after
 wall built.

Close cavities at eaves level, ensuring a level bed for the wall plate
Consider verge and gable finish and the building in of straps and ties.

Dpcs and lintels
Ensure horizontal and vertical dpcs and trays join
Bed and level lintels properly and allow for settlement.

Floor joists
Allow tolerances when building in
Level and pack accurately and tightly
Ensure joists are seated firmly in hangers
Treat joists ends.

Separating walls
Ensure joints are made soundly
Consider scaffolding problems.

Partitions
Avoid making loadbearing where possible by clear spanning floors between
    external walls
Build or tie in properly
Consider buildability, especially the use of platforms and trestles.

Infill panels
Consider tolerances and allow for differential expansion
Provide expansion joints
Avoid the use of brick and tile slips, unless 'mechanically' supported.

Other factors
Consider brick specification and brickwork quality below ground (dpc) level
Ensure labour skill levels are adequate for the quality of work in hand
Supervise properly
Protect new brickwork from staining and damage.

References

[26]BDA, *Bricks and brickwork on site*, BDA 1979
[27]BRE, *Various Digests on bricks and brickwork*, HMSO
[28]Tovey, A K, *Concrete masonry for the contractor*, C & CA
[29]BRE, *Mortars for bricklaying*, Digest 160, HMSO
[30]Brick Development Association, *Mortars for brickwork*, BDA Practical Note No. 2, BDA, 1973
[31]BRE/DoE, *External masonry cavity walls : wall ties – installation*, DAS 20, BRE
[32]BRE/DoE, *External masonry walls insulated with mineral fibre cavity-width batts : resisting rain penetration*, DAS 17, BRE
[33]TRADA, *Floors above ground floors*, IBL 51/5, TRADA
[34]BDA, *Brickwork cladding to multi-storey reinforced concrete framed structures*, TN9, BDA, 1975

(viii) Superstructures: timber Timber superstructures may be divided into two general categories, as far as UK practice is concerned (balloon frames, common elsewhere, for example in the USA, are not usual in the UK): 'platform' frames and 'true' frames of post and beam type, which use special timber components such as laminated and built-up beams and portals.

Timber platform frame[35,36]   Now commonly used in low-rise, short-span buildings up to three storeys; fire regulations prevent their economic use above this height. Quality on site depends upon efficient design, correct handling and storage, accurate erection of the basic frame and carefully fixed cladding and internal linings.

Design should be carried out in sympathy with the material and with the building technique. For example, it is usually undesirable to convert a masonry design to timber frame, tempted by the apparent adaptability of the material. This is because timber panels are most economic when modular, that is when variety reduction is practised, since they are made up in jigs which should not be altered more often than necessary. A wide variety of panels leads to complication on site, for example in the identification of panels and to problems of jointing: many jointing conditions may occur and quality of work may suffer in consequence. The possibility of large panel design should be considered. Where complete walls can be made in the shop, quality within the perimeter of each panel can be controlled at shop tolerances: this may be important in the case of openings in panels, in linings and sheathings and in the provision of services, which may be pre-fixed *(6.20)*. Large panels require delivery on low-loaders and handling by crane, and plant must be able to reach the building under construction. This may require temporary road construction, unless permanent roads have been laid prior to shell erection.

Designers should consider the problem of labour skill levels and 'fixability'. Can reasonable skill levels be relied upon (here the choice of contractor may be critical) and will it be physically possible to assemble certain components on site? How can correct assembly be ensured? As with other components, timber panels should be stored for a minimum time on site and should be handled with care. Financially, a building must be built and yielding a return as quickly as possible once the land, materials and labour are paid for. Direct assembly from the delivery vehicle is desirable, therefore, which in turn implies accurate ordering and firmly agreed delivery dates. This may be difficult if there are problems below ground, which have caused unforeseen delays in the programme. To obviate this, 'dry' or piled foundations should be considered, especially where site conditions are uncertain.

Storage of timber components should be such as to prevent them going into bow and twist and absorbing undue quantities of moisture, for example, by storing under cover and ventilating.

Handling, whether manually or by crane, should not risk damage from impact or, more serious, from straining joints by lifting at the incorrect nodes or by carrying flat rather than vertically.

Frame erection[36]   Before assembly of the timber superstructure begins, it is important that the substructure is level and that final adjustment of the sole plate to within ± 6mm is possible with only slight variations in bedding material. The dpc should be placed and bedded and agreement should be reached with the timber frame supplier that the setting out is correct and that levels are within tolerance. Services below the slab and drainage connections should be completed before erection begins. Superstructure panels are then either manhandled into position, or, in the case of large panels or large sub-assemblies, lifted into position by crane. Nailing must be carried out according to the nailing schedule and preferably in dry conditions, with panels

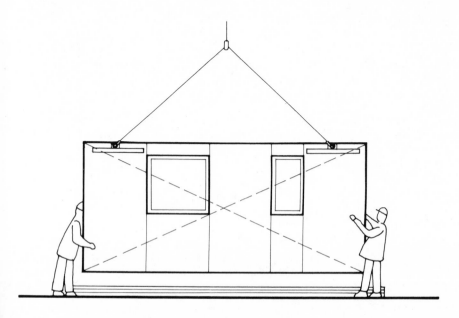

crane handling a large panel fabricated in the shop

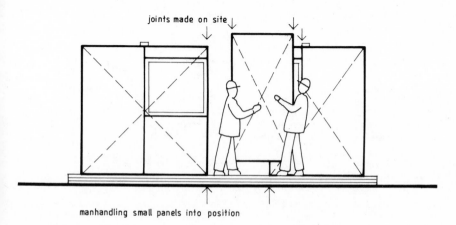

manhandling small panels into position

6.20   *Large panels improve quality: fewer joints necessary*

6.21 *Timber Platform frame: quality factors*

carefully supported with timber props. Head binders should overlap panel joints and should be fixed once panels are self supporting and plumb. Fixing the floor deck should only be carried out in dry conditions to minimise shrinkage and damage, especially likely with particle board materials. If concealed pipework is fixed at this stage, care should be taken to protect any pipe tails projecting through the deck. After erection of the first floor panels, it is important to fix the eaves head binder and complete the roofing of the building as quickly as possible to protect the vulnerable deck and to allow any damp panels to dry out before internal lining begins. It is sufficient to felt and batten the roof and to fix the breather paper to the sheathing, but a better job would include glazing and hanging the external doors.

Cladding and lining   It is important to ensure that the basic frame is secure before commencing cladding and lining and that there has been no random drilling of studs and joists *(6.21)*. Services, cavity barriers and fire-stops should be fixed and rubbish should be cleared from inside panels. Insulation mats should be fitted into panels leaving no gaps. Vapour checks should then be stapled to the frame, with care taken to avoid puncturing. Note that vapour checks should only be fixed when the moisture content of the timber has dropped below 18–20%: this may be difficult in wet weather, and after roofing and glazing it may be necessary to de-humidify the building or to leave a period for drying out before fixing the lining. Cladding must be tied back securely to the frame. This is easy if using profiled boarding on battens or tile-hanging, since mechanical fixings will be used at every stage: the major problem on site will be correct setting out of the boarding or sheeting and the forming of end joints and corners. With masonry cladding[37], ties must be provided at the correct centres and nailed securely into the studs (not into the sheathing only); this is made easier for the bricklayer if the positions of the studs are marked clearly on the breather paper or if the ties are pre-fixed.

Other timber structures   These are usually pre-fabricated off-site and, where larger than the delivery vehicle can transport, are delivered in sections.

Erection procedure requires accurate setting out and levelling of substructures and careful lifting and placing using a crane of the appropriate capacity. Where vision from the crane is restricted, the banksman should be experienced and trustworthy. Jointing, apart from being structurally sound, should utilise man-handleable fixings such as bolts. The safety of operatives during this work is important and provision should be made for gantries, safety harnesses and protective clothing. After fixing frames, check measurements of the spacings between frame members should be made to compare with designed sizes of infill panels, claddings and any secondary structures, such as purlins and structural sheeting.

Summary of factors affecting quality:
Timber platform frame[38]
Design
To be in sympathy with the building technique and with the panel system
  being adopted

Consider panel modules and grids
Try to achieve variety reduction
Consider large panels or large sub-assemblies, which save time on site
Consider labour skill levels and fixability

Delivery
Consider possible need for police escorts for wide and bulky loads and timing
of delivery to ensure rapid off-loading and placing.

Storage
Ensure correct methods of storage are used
Minimise time in storage
Control moisture content

Handling
Decide whether to be manual or by crane
Avoid impact damage
Avoid straining joints

Erection
Ensure levels are correct
Plumb panels and prop during fixing
Use nailing schedules
Fix deck and protect from wetting
Protect services
Enclose structure as quickly as possible.

Cladding
Ensure this is tied back to the frame
Mark positions of studs when fixing wall ties
Fix cavity barriers and fire stops.

Lining
Check moisture content[39]
Ensure frame is complete and that surfaces are level
Clean out panels
Fix insulation tight in frame
Lap and staple vapour check
Avoid puncturing.

Timber structures
Ensure correct off-site manufacture of frame members
Set out and level, lift and place accurately
Check accuracy after assembly.

References
[35]TRADA/NBA, *Timber frame housing – a simplified method*, Contruction Press
[36]TRADA, *Site guidance : timber frame houses*, TBL 56, TRADA
[37]BDA, *Brick cladding to timer frame construction*, DN6, BDA, 1982

[38]TRADA, *Timber frame construction : site check list*, Wood Information Sheet 0–8, TRADA
[39]BRE, *Drying out buildings*, Digest 163, HMSO

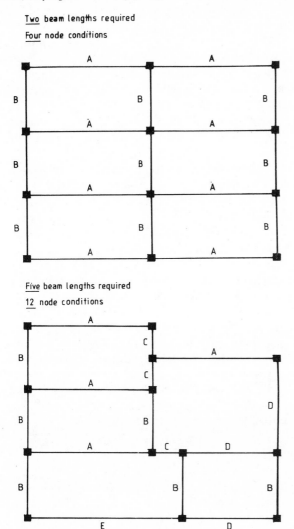

Two beam lengths required

Four node conditions

Five beam lengths required

12 node conditions

6.22   *Variety reduction: beam lengths in framed structures*

(ix) Superstructure: steel frame   Design affects the quality of steel frame construction in several ways[40]. If the design takes no account of variety reduction, there will be a multitude of different sizes and lengths of stanchions and beams and many different types of fixings. The engineer responsible for the design of the structure may have no greater regard for reduction in variety than the architect *(6.22)*. This will lead to complex ordering and delivery schedules and the possible delay in delivery of more complex components. If delays occur because components are not available, the steel erectors may

71

have to return for a second or third visit, which is expensive.

The same principles for setting out, levelling and erection apply as for timber framed structures, that is accuracy and care in handling and post-erection measurement to cross-check against sizes ordered for secondary structures, infillings and claddings. Erection plant is likely to be of critical importance: where mobile plant is used, it must be able to get to within working distance of the building and components must not exceed the safe working capacity of the plant. Where erection plant is fixed, for example where tower cranes are being used, the initial erection and dismantling of this plant should be considered from a very early stage. Cranes should be located where they can provide maximum service to the site, for example when using precast concrete frame and cladding systems, when all major components are crane hoisted.

With steel frame construction, where casing using either concrete or dry systems is required for the protection of the primary structural members, cranes will be employed in lifting formwork, reinforcement, concrete, and dry materials to higher levels in the building and will be needed for this purpose. They may also be needed for cladding panels, major services components, such as lift machinery, and internal partitions and linings.

Jointing of steel structures is carried out by bolting or welding. Welding on site is undesirable, owing to the difficulty of carrying out the work to designed standards in exposed locations, and bolting is therefore most usual. Accuracy of erection is essential, however, to ensure bolt holes line up and that extra drilling on site is minimised. Other major factors in quality control, apart from a good erection gang and variety reduction, are accurate design, shop priming or de-rusting and scaling before delivery and touching up damaged areas after erection.

On site storage of steel components should avoid stressing members unduly and should in any case be minimised, to ensure least financial on-cost and degradation of the steel.

Summary of 'quality' points on steel frames
Design
Consider variety reduction, to simplify assembly, reduce the risk of error, reduce costs and ease ordering and delivery.

On site
Consider the use of dry casings and intumescent coatings for fire protection rather than of in situ concrete[41]
Ensure setting out and levelling of frames is done accurately
During erection, consider most effective use of plant, whether mobile or fixed; make use of its versatility, for example by using cranes for other parts of the building process
When bolting members, consider tolerance and accuracy of fit
Avoid site welding where possible
Programming of erection should aim for smooth sequencing and cladding to ensure an enclosed and dry envelope as soon in the job as possible.

Consider storage

Minimise, to reduce financial outlay and degradation of steel; shop prime, de-rust or scale before erection.

Labour

Safety of operatives should be considered and erection gangs must be properly trained.

Other points

Accurate levelling and erection is made easier if stanchion bases are accurately positioned and levelled. Base plates should be grouted after structure has been plumbed, lined and bolted up.

References

[40]BSI, *The use of structural steel in building*, British Standard 449: Pt. 2: 1969, BSI

[41]Smith, C I, *Fire protection of structural steel in multi-storey buildings*, British Steel Corporation

(x) Superstructure: concrete frame: in situ reinforced Quality in reinforced concrete construction of frames has two main elements: the quality of concrete used and the quality of formwork.

Concrete quality[42,43]

This depends to a great extent on the use of good quality materials, accurately proportioned, with the right amount of water added, followed by thorough mixing. The mixed concrete is then placed in well made formwork, with tight fitting joints, in which the reinforcement has been correctly positioned. Thorough compaction of the concrete resulting in even density and a good surface finish should be the objective.

Testing and checking of all the above stages is essential, with slump and cube tests taken at regular intervals.

Materials should comply with the relevant BSSs and suppliers should be able to guarantee that their materials do so comply. On site, the following points are important:

Cement

(a) Keep dry at all times.

(b) Do not hold excessive stocks, since cement deteriorates with age.

(c) Store different types of cement separately to avoid wrong use.

Sand and aggregates

(a) There should be a properly constructed storage area on site, which will ensure aggregates are kept clean and free from impurities.

(b) Storage areas should allow the different aggregates to be kept separate from each other.

Accurate proportioning of materials is gauged either by volume or by weight. The materials are measured either in accurately sized and constructed gauge boxes, when mixing by volume, or on calibrated weight batching equipment.

The amount of water added should be adjusted either daily or delivery by delivery, depending upon which is the shorter period; the moisture content of the aggregates must be allowed for when adding water.

The materials should be mixed for a set period of time, before discharging from the mixer into a suitable container for transporting to the work-place. Whatever means are used to transport the concrete, they should not allow the concrete to dry out, to segregate or to consolidate. The mixed concrete should be placed within 30 minutes of being mixed.

Formwork[44] Formwork should contain the correct reinforcement, properly bent and tied with spacers to ensure that the required cover is maintained. This can only be checked by comparing the reinforcement with the bending schedules and drawings and by examining it in position to ensure that there is no rust, scale, dirt or grease on the bars and that they are unable to move during concreting. The formwork should be constructed with tight fitting joints, to ensure grout is not lost, and should be braced to withstand bulging, displacement and vibration, especially at the bottom of deep forms where pressure is greatest. Struts and walings should therefore be placed to ensure that deflection of the forms does not take place during placing. Formwork should be clean and free from dirt and rubbish and surfaces in contact with the concrete should be treated with a mould oil or similar to facilitate stripping. Mould oil should not come into contact with steel reinforement. Shuttering should only be stripped after the specified period for curing has elapsed. This is related to the time taken for the setting process to reach the point where the concrete will retain its form without external support and concrete should be supported to avoid stresses until the design strength has been achieved. Design of formwork should ensure that it is easy to strip and unlikely to cause damage to the surface of the concrete during removal.

Placing Concrete should be placed in a continuous operation up to the required level in the formwork, ensuring that it is thoroughly compacted around reinforcement and reaches all corners. The top surface should be finished as specified and the concrete then protected during the initial set from the effects of sun, drying winds and frost. Protection is also required from running water and impact. With normal mixes, curing should last for approximately seven days. This will prevent the surface of the concrete from drying out too quickly, which can result in shrinkage cracking.

Other points Concreting should not take place when there is a danger of freezing or when heavy frosts are expected.

Testing of concrete is important and is required for:
(a) Moisture content
(b) Slump. Concrete cubes will also be required, to test for strength as the concrete matures.

Where concrete is supplied ready-mixed, inspection of plant and testing and mixing methods must be carried out by a competent person. Long lorry hauls should be avoided and it is important not to over- or under-order if waste or unwanted joints are to be avoided.

Safety for operatives, especially at high level, is important. This implies proper training of operatives, the use of correct clothing, including protective head and footwear, and the use of safety harnesses, in addition to scaffolding.

Summary of points affecting in situ reinforced concrete frames
Concrete quality
Consider mix design and quality of materials
Storage of aggregates and cement
Mixing methods; proportioning of mixes
Handling, especially across site
Lifting and pouring: ensure correct use of plant and equipment
Allow for protection and curing.

Testing
Carry out regular tests including: slump and cube, to measure water content
and crushing strength.

Formwork
Ensure properly constructed
Make repetitive use of where possible, which affects the materials used in its
manufacture
Consider ease of erection and striking, including interior projections, mould
oils, and external support systems
Consider materials in relation to the finish required
Consider special forms: slip shuttering, etc.

Reinforcement
Design correctly
Is prefabrication possible?
Can areas of reinforcement be standardised?
Protect against corrosion; clean before use
Cut using shearing cutters rather than by burning
Check specification upon delivery, ensuring, for example, correct identifica-
tion of mild and high tensile steel and that cut and bent steel has been
correctly labelled.

Placing concrete
Ensure continuous pours and, if ready-mixed, that correct quantities have
been ordered
Make correct use of plant and labour
Compact properly round reinforcement and ensure that formwork is properly
filled
Do not place in cold weather: check temperatures
Consider construction and daywork joints.

Labour and supervision
Provide skilled superivision
Check the safety and skill levels of operatives.

References
[42]Blackledge, G F, *Man on the job* (MoJ) leaflets, C & CA
[43]Cement and Concrete Association, *Concrete practice*, C & CA
[44]Austin, C K, *Site Carpentry*, Northwood, 1979

Precast concrete frames[56]   These have many similarities to steel frames, in that construction is dry, components being cast in the factory or at ground level and lifted into position by crane. If cast in the factory, transportation will dictate the maximum component size, although quality will be higher with factory-cast units, despite a risk of damage during transportation and handling. Repetition of shapes and sizes is essential to minimise costs, but high quality finishes to components is possible. The storage of components prior to fixing should be minimised, since the space occupied can be expensive and can take up valuable room on site.

Pre-cast work is specialised and is therefore usually sub-contracted: this requires skilled management input to minimise problems and to ensure a smooth work-flow. The sequence of assembly of frames is important. Extensive in situ work should be avoided where a frame is pre-cast and designers should ensure that buildings are one or the other, whilst recognising the unavoidable need for in situ work in such stages and elements as floor topping, bedding and stair and lift towers.

Setting out, levelling and checking are as important as with timber and steel frames, and the same principles apply (See (ix)). Erection plant is equally critical and the design should be conceived with the system of erection very much in mind. Column and beam sections and panels require careful lifting to avoid overstressing, accurate placing and temporary propping during the fixing process, which can involve the placing of in situ concrete round continuity reinforcement and the grouting of panel beds and joints. To this end, mix design, manufacture and placing have a vital role to play. During erection, work should be protected and further cleaning may be necessary after completion.

Expert labour and supervison of the placing and fixing of precast units is essential. Safety of operatives is also of paramount importance.

Summary of points
Manufacture
Usually in the factory, where high quality is possible
Transportation limits the size and weights of components
It is important to avoid damage during transit and off-loading.

Erection
Lifting and placing should be direct from delivery vehicles if possible *(6.03)*
Storage should be minimised
Care should be taken when lifting to avoid stressing panels and sections
Temporary propping of components will usually be needed
Reinforcement continuity will require careful placing of both steel and in situ
   concrete

Bedding and grouting: mix design is important

Protection of work during erection and cleaning after completion may be necessary. Labour and supervision: supply and erection is usually a sub-contract item; management should take account of this when considering quality levels.

Other points

Avoid mixing precast with in situ work wherever possible, although this will be unavoidable at certain stages of work and for certain elements

Consider safety of operatives.

Reference

[45]PCFA, *Precast Concrete Frame Association*: various publications, PCFA

(xi) Superstructures: upper floors   The following flooring systems will be considered as being typical of modern construction:

Timber joisted, with deck

Precast: beams and 'pots'
        prestressed planks;

In situ: single and two-way span, 'T'-beams, 'waffle' slabs.

Timber joisted[46]   This is the usual form of construction for low-rise, short-span structures. Timber must be correctly stored to minimise damage and to control moisture content. Care must be taken to avoid timbers in twist, bow or warp *(6.23)*. Joists may have to be levelled and packed to obtain correct room heights and level ceilings and floors. They must be strapped to external walls and ends must be treated where built in[47]. They should seat tightly upon hangers and shoes, which should in turn be fixed tight against walls to ensure structural continuity. Notching should be avoided and only the neutral axes drilled for services. Solid bridging or strutting may be needed on longer spans; note that proprietary metal strutting can save time and be easier to fix *(6.13)*. Where there are openings, the lengths of trimming joists should be minimised, for example by arranging for openings to run in the direction of the span *(6.24)*.

Services provide access to pipes and wiring for fixing and later maintenance. Minimise the provision of areas within the floor thickness for drainage, for example from showers and baths, since joists may have to be cut and trimmed round.

Partitions allow for double-joisting or the provision of RSJs under first floor partitions where spans are long. Careful design can eliminate the need for such support, for example by placing partitions over supporting walls or by limiting spans.

Floor decks[48] are formed from boarded or sheet materials. Softwood, t and g boarding is nearly as fast for a skilled carpenter to lay as chipboard or plywood sheeting, and has better resistance to wetting. The sheet materials are faster to lay where floor plans are simple in shape. They are ideal, therefore, for timber platform frame construction, where there are no

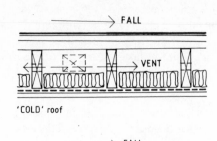

A   'COLD' roof

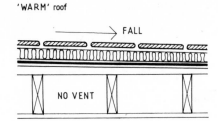

B   'WARM' roof

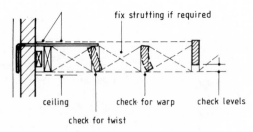

C   'INVERTED' roof

Types of flat roof construction

'QUALITY' factors

A
Provide protective surface
Specify and fix membranes correctly
Correct material for deck; use interlocking
                                    sheets
Lay to even and adequate falls
Ventilate structure
Insulate tightly
Lap and seal vapour check ; do not puncture

B
As above BUT
Avoid damaging insulation during fixing
DO NOT ventilate structure

C
As above

* see Drawing 6.13 for summary of quality
  factors on plan

Flat roof types

fix straps and pack tightly

fix strutting if required

check for deflection

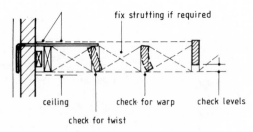

ceiling   check for warp   check levels

check for twist

Faults in timber roof construction

check moisture content of timber before
lining in

6.23   Floors and flat roofs: timber; quality factors

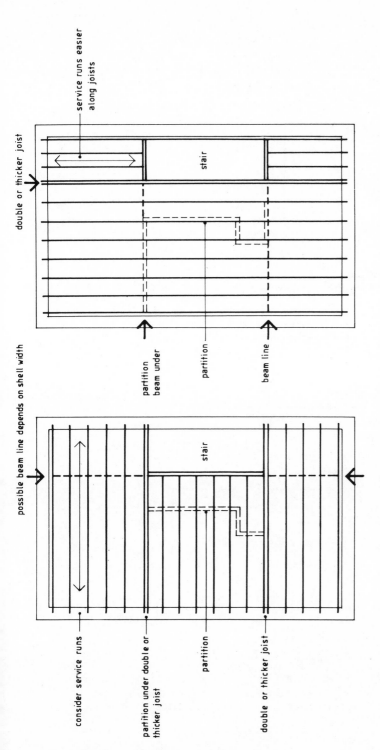

Consider economy and efficiency of joist layout in relation to shell dimensions, opening sizes and positions and locations of supporting elements
Consider service runs and location of first floor partitions

6.24 *Floors: alternative joist layouts*

79

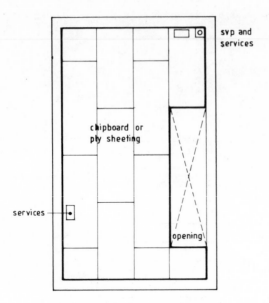

svp and
services

chipboard or
ply sheeting

services

opening

For simple plans, dimensionally rationalised to suit sheet sizes, ply or
chipboard sheets are most suitable. Good for timber frame.
Plan service accesses and protect against wetting

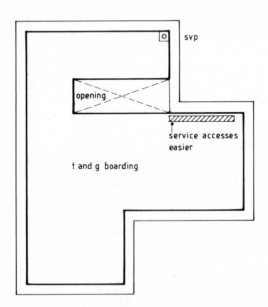

svp

opening

service accesses
easier

t and g boarding

for complex plans, t and g boarding may be better. boarding allows
service accesses to be made more easily and has good resistance to
wetting

6.25   *Floors: alternative decking systems*

80

external walls or partitions above floor level to obstruct laying *(6.25)*. Chipboard sheets especially can be degraded by moisture before the structure has been enclosed[49]. Correct storage of sheets and of chipboard is important, since they are more easily damaged by rough handling[50]. Joists and decking are normally fixed and laid manually, although where a crane is available, as in large panel construction, complete floor sections may be made up off site or at ground level and lifted into position with the crane; since there are fewer joints, this can improve quality and save time, important in poor weather. With both types of deck, service routes should be planned before assembly and all necessary access panels provided.

Pre-cast floors: beams and pots Suitable for larger span construction, this composite floor contains a mixture of at least three components: precast concrete beams, precast infill units and in situ fill and/or topping *(6.09)*. There may also be steel reinforcement, for example to provide continuity over load-bearing walls. Because of the composite nature of the construction, quality control may be harder to maintain than with simple floors such as timber joisted or prestressed planks. Several different components and materials must be ordered, delivered, stored and handled. For example, the precast units must be ordered, cast in the factory, delivered to site, lifted by crane and placed in position, where their setting out is critical, since otherwise the infill units will not fit. The infill units, clay or clinker 'pots' or special concrete blocks, must be delivered, off-loaded and stored until required and then lifted in batches to the working level, where they must be placed between the precast beams. Finally, after any reinforcement has been fixed, concrete must be mixed, placed in the spaces between pots and planks and allowed to harden, before a final topping layer is poured. This must be allowed to set before the floor can be used for further constructional work, causing sometimes substantial delay. It will be apparent why quality control of this form of construction can be difficult: the different components and materials each require specialised treatment and there are varying time intervals between the placing of the dry materials, the pouring of the concrete and the completion of the floor. Further problems can be caused by the provision of services, especially by service drops through the thickness of the floor, and by the large amounts of moisture which the floors contain, leading to long delays in drying out. Unplanned loading of upper floors, for example by partitions, can also cause 'hogging' over supporting elements and partitions below, resulting in structural failure.

Pre-cast floors; prestressed planks These are suitable for short or medium span floors *(6.26)*. They are simpler than beam and pot, since only the planks are required to complete the floor. A topping is required with some systems to add strength, ensure structural continuity across the floor and to satisfy fire regulations. Where this is not required, as with ground floors in domestic buildings, the floor can be used immediately after placing. Units must be cast and post-tensioned or pre-stressed in the factory, and care must be taken to avoid excessive camber or 'hogging' which can cause problems with levels and screed thicknesses; this places a limitation on span owing to difficulties in transportation. Planks must be lifted carefully by crane and placed on true and level bearings. Placing direct from the delivery vehicle is desirable. Sometimes an in situ topping and reinforcement are necessary, for example where floors are continuous over load-bearing walls. This requires a separate operation to mix and pour the concrete and prevents floors being used immediately. Provision of services can be more difficult even than with 'beam and pot' and other in situ systems, since the prestressed units must not be damaged near the prestressing wires; this can inhibit the routeing of pipes, conduit and wiring, the positions of which must be carefully planned. Another problem arises from the modular nature of the units. They can only be used efficiently over rectangular bays: irregularly shaped corners must be

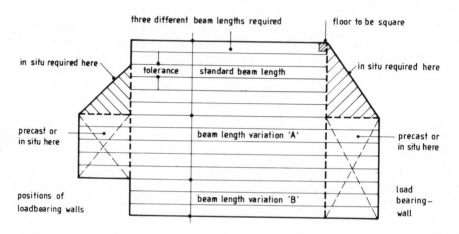

complex plans require a mix of precast and in situ construction :
AVOID if possible

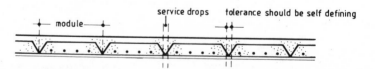

prestressed planks with topping : delay in access until topping set

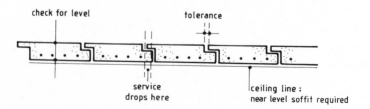

planks with no topping : immediate access

6.26   *Precast, prestressed concrete planks*

82

formed in some other way, usually with in situ concrete, which must be shuttered and poured as a separate and time-consuming operation *(6.26)*.

In situ floors: beam and slab[51,52] The traditional concrete floor, where bay size and shape dictate the type of span, whether one- or two-way construction, requires both floor and edge shuttering, sound design and accurate placing of both reinforcement and concrete. Most of the points covering concrete mix, reinforcement and placing made under 'Concrete in situ frames' apply to in situ floor construction. These include concrete quality, testing, formwork and reinforcement, with the labour-critical element of placing and supervision. Formwork design may not have to take into account such a high degree of surface finish, since there will be both floor and ceiling finishes in most cases, although supporting the floor during pouring and setting may require a large number of props. This will in turn obstruct the working space below, necessitating careful pre-planning of the work sequence. Owing to the loads involved, it is often necessary to support the new floor on floors below, with continuous support sometimes down to ground level. Services can be a problem and must be pre-planned, with drop-boxes and ducts cast in where needed.

An alternative to conventional shuttering is the use of a patent system, of which the 'waffle' slab is an example, which provides both structural strength and a self-finished ceiling to the floor below. Essentially, the 'waffle' consists of two-way 'T'-beams, the spaces between 'Ts' being formed by glass-fibre moulds. These give a smooth and interesting gridded effect to the ceiling. Moulds must be carefully stored and handled to prevent damage to what will be the finished surface, and striking the shuttering is equally important for the same reason.

Summary of 'quality' points in floor construction
Timber joisted
Ensure correct storage of timber and components; control moisture content
Place and level joists and fix tight to walls
Plan service routes and pre-drill for services before assembly
Use bridging and strutting where necessary
Form openings parallel to joist spans where possible
Allow for partitions and other exceptional loadings
Floor decks: decide whether to use boarding or sheeting; protect against
    damage and excessive wetting; form accesses for services
Check labour skill levels; ensure proper supervision
Consider the use of pre-fabricated flooring units, lifted by crane.

Pre-cast: beam and 'pot' systems
Remember that several different materials and components have to be
    stored, handled and placed, making quality control more difficult
Allow for tolerances between units, levelling and over-stressing due to
    unforeseen loads; reduce water content as much as possible to speed drying
    out

Allow for delay in carrying out further work while concrete matures
Check labour skill levels; ensure proper supervision
Design for services distribution.

Pre-cast: prestressed beams and planks
Simpler than beam and pot; tolerances less critical and can be self-defining
Transportation should be considered and crane handling will be necessary
In situ or screeded topping and reinforcement may be required
Since units are modular, they suit rectangular bays; odd shaped bays must be
    cast in situ
Make provision for service drops and horizontal distribution of services across
    the floor.

In situ: beam and slab
The same quality problems occur as with in situ frames: concrete quality,
    testing, formwork and reinforcement should be given first consideration
Check labour skill levels; ensure proper supervision
Floor shuttering must be fully supported and supports can obstruct workng on
    lower floors; consider work sequence
Upper floors may have to be propped on lower ones; support may have to be
    continuous down to ground level
Consider using cement-rich concrete to permit earlier striking of formwork
Services locations must be pre-planned
Consider the use of patent shuttering systems, such as trough decking or
    'waffle' grids
Storage, handling and striking of special floor shuttering units can be critical.

Other points
Designers should consider:
    – loadings
    – sound insulation
    – speed of erection of formwork, placing concrete and striking of
      formwork
    – floor shape and area
    – services
    – ceiling type and finish required below slab.
Contractors should consider:
    – type of formwork: appropriate detailing and construction
    – possible use of patented or reusable systems
    – methods of lifting concrete to upper floor levels
    – work sequence, especially where formwork will obstruct lower floors.

References
[46]TRADA, Floors above ground floors, TBL 51/5, TRADA
[47]BRE/DoE, *External and separating walls: lateral restraint at intermediate timber floors – installation*, DAS 26, BRE
[48]BRE/DoE, *Suspended timber floors : chipboard flooring – storage and installation*, DAS 32, BRE
[49]BRE, *The use of chipboard*, Digest 239, HMSO

[50]TRADA, *Care of timber and wood-based sheet materials on building sites*, Wood Information Sheet 4–12, TRADA

[51]Blackledge, G F, *Man on the job* (MoJ) leaflets, Nos. 1–18, C & CA

[52]C & CA, *Pumped concrete* (reprint 3/80), C & CA

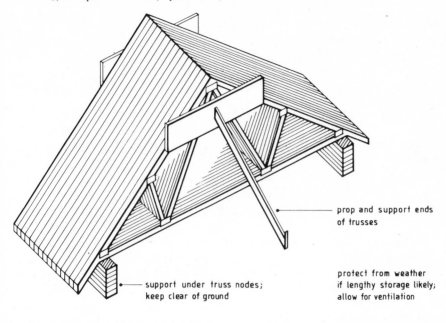

prop and support ends of trusses

protect from weather if lengthy storage likely; allow for ventilation

vertical storage

support under truss nodes; keep clear of ground

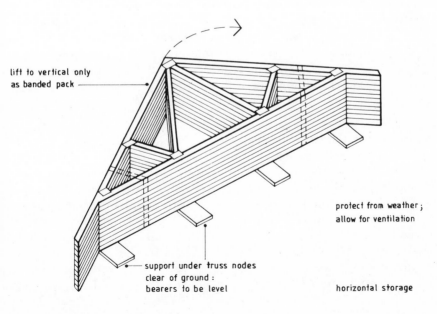

lift to vertical only as banded pack

protect from weather; allow for ventilation

support under truss nodes clear of ground : bearers to be level

horizontal storage

6.27 *Storing timber-roof-trusses on site*

85

(xii) Superstructures: roofing systems   The following roofing systems will be
considered as being typical of modern construction:

Timber	Trussed rafter
	Purlin and rafter
	Joisted (flat)
Steel	Lattice beam
	Portal
	Other, eg monitor, north-light
Concrete	In situ: slab and beam
	Precast

NB   Finishes are dealt with in sections (xiii) and (xiv).

Timber: trussed rafter   Some of the quality factors affecting the design and
installation of trussed rafters have already been discussed. Trusses are very
susceptible to strain and damage since they have no resistance to bending
normal to the truss plane. To work efficiently in the roof, they must be
correctly located on the wall-plates, which must be level and firmly bedded,
and fixed to both the wall-plates and gables with steel straps and ties. They
must also be braced against wind-loads.

After manufacture, trusses are carried to the site by lorry. They must be
off-loaded carefully, either manually or by crane, slinging only from the node
points, and checked for quality especially in the timber and the gang nail
plates. Storage[53] should be vertical wherever possible, with the trusses
supported clear of the ground on their node points and banded together
(6.27). Protection from the weather is essential: dry conditions can cause
timber to split and shake, wet conditions can result in warping and twisting. It
is usual to manhandle single trusses of modest span to roof level, but groups
of trusses are lifted by crane when one is available. Again, trusses should be
kept vertical to avoid strain. Trusses are spaced out along the wall-plates and
tied temporarily to gable and party walls, to the wall-plates and to each other
during fixing. Good co-ordination with the bricklayers is essential to ensure
that wall-plates, ties and straps are built in correctly[54-56].

Purlins and rafters are an alternative form of pitched roof structure *(6.28)*.
Built-up or solid timber beams and purlins are fixed between gable or party
walls to provide support for rafters at mid or part-span. These members are
made in the factory and transported to site by lorry. The same problems of
handling and storage apply as with trussed rafters, except that purlins and
beams are less susceptible to damage during handling. Larger units must be
lifted into position by crane. Location and levelling of purlins are critical and
this requires exceptional care from the carpenters; errors will result in
incorrect location of the rafters and set up localised stresses in the structure
once the roof is loaded.

Rafters must be free of twist and warp and be of the correct stress grading.
They must be stored correctly under cover, usually in the compound to
reduce the risk of damage and theft.

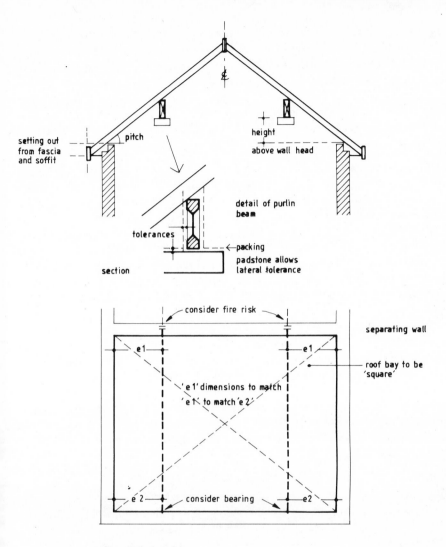

setting out
from fascia
and soffit

pitch

height
above wall head

detail of purlin
beam

tolerances

packing

padstone allows
lateral tolerance

section

consider fire risk

separating wall

e1

e1

roof bay to be
'square'

'e1'dimensions to match
'e1' to match'e2'

e2

consider bearing

e2

plan : typical roof bay

6.28   *Roofs: purlin beams; setting out*

Fixings must be of the appropriate type and used correctly to prevent movement in the rafters and to provide proper resistance to wind loads.

Joisted (flat) roofs[57,58]   Many of the same quality points apply as for 'timber joisted floors' (see (xi)) *(6.13)* and elsewhere regarding the proper treatment of timber: joists must be of the correct stress grading, be carefully handled and stored and be placed according to the design requirements. Joists are laid dead level and falls are built up either by using timber firrings or by fixing insulation moulded to form falls. The roof structure should be strutted where spans are long and strapped back to external walls and to the supporting structure below.

Decking may be of plywood, particle board or of 'sandwiches', which combine both insulation and damp proof membranes. All require tight jointing and fixing at correct centres to ensure true and level surfaces. With 'cold' roofs, ventilation must be provided, both across the direction of span and from end to end *(6.23)*. Co-ordination between carpenters and bricklayers is essential to ensure correct tolerances and levels and the proper completion of eaves and verges. Joisted roofs should not be enclosed until moisture in the timber has reached the correct levels, usually below 20%.

Steel roofs: lattice beam   These are a common form of structural support for low-rise, medium span roofs. Many of the quality points already discussed in 'Superstructure: steel frame' (see (iv)) apply. These include variety reduction, whose purpose is to reduce the number of different lengths and sizes of beams required *(6.22)*, accurate setting out and levelling, although at roof level this will be pre-determined to a large extent by the supporting structure. Cranes will always be needed for lifting and placing and attention should be given to the jointing of the beam to the main structure, and to minimal stockpiling of components, to reduce both financial on-costs and the risks of corrosion.

The advantages of steel lattice beams and purlins are their low weight in relation to span and their suitability for flat- or very low-pitched roofs on light-weight structures. The beams are manufactured off-site, sometimes in sections where spans are long, and should ideally be placed and fixed directly from the delivery vehicle. They may require protection against damage and corrosion. Fixing requires care from erection teams and good supervision to ensure close tolerances, important for easy later fixing of any secondary structure such as steel purlins, sheeting rails and troughed metal decking.

Steel roofs: portal frames are another common form for medium-span light-weight buildings, where low-pitched roofs and floors unobstructed by columns are required. Sections are manufactured off-site and assembled on arrival *(6.29)*. Erection requires a crane of appropriate capacity and radius of lift and accurate levelling of bases is essential to ensure easy assembly. This is carried out either by welding or bolting, usually the latter. Most 'quality' points are the same as for other steel structures, but there should be particular regard to the need for accurate plumbing and lining through before cladding is fixed.

Other steel roofs: monitor, north-light etc   Applications for these roof types are usually industrial, where good natural lighting and clear spans over working floors are a design requirement. Because of the size of the structures, assembly on site will be from a relatively large number of components. Such assembly requires great accuracy in setting out, especially in the supporting frame and sub-structures. Crane handling of components is necessary and, as with other steelwork, site welding should be minimised. Since there is a close relationship between primary and secondary structures, which include purlins, decking systems and glazing, accurate plumbing and lining through are essential.

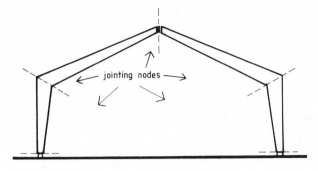

standard method of erecting portal frame on site

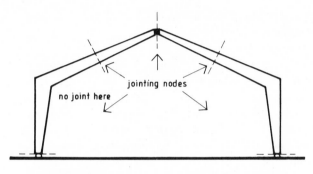

preferred method of jointing, respecting bending moments
of the structure

erection of frame may be more difficult using this system

sectional lengths and weights should take account of transportation
difficulties

6.29   *Portal roofs: handling and erection*

Concrete roofs: in situ slab and beam[59] Owing to the weight of these roofs,
they are usually only used where substantial access to the roof is required or
where spans are modest. Wet construction can lead to problems of drying out
and to movement and failure in the roof finishes. Thermal efficiency is
important, therefore, and warm or 'inverted' roof construction should be
considered with the main roof structure contained within the building's
thermal envelope *(6.23)*. Most of the points made in the section on concrete
floors apply to concrete roofs (see (xi)). For example, concrete quality is of
paramount importance, as are the testing of materials and mixes, formwork
and reinforcement. To ensure standards are met, good quality labour and
supervision are important. Shuttering for the roof must be supported, often
down through the building, which can disturb work below unless 'flying'
shutters are used; these carry the concrete and formwork loads across the roof
onto the loadbearing frame of the building. Horizontal and vertical

89

distribution of services must be planned to avoid interference with reinforcement.

Concrete roofs: precast   These include precast beams, with decking units, or precast slabs. Both may require in situ or screeded toppings laid to falls. Their advantages are the rapid completion rate possible and the early enclosing of the structure, together with the elimination of formwork, with all its associated props and supports. Other quality points are the same as for precast frame construction described in section (xi): these include the need for mechanical handling of units, the probable mix of precast and in situ work, where bay shapes are irregular, and topping layers, requiring delivery of in situ concrete sometimes to high levels in the building. Proper provision for services must be made, especially where units are prestressed.

Summary of quality points in roof construction
Timber: trussed rafter
Transport and off-load vertically
Stack vertically or horizontally in banded packs and support on nodes
Lift and handle without straining plates; if stored horizontally, lift only as a
  banded pack *(6.27)*
Protect against unduly dry or wet conditions and control moisture content;
  allow wet timber to dry before completing roof
Carpenters to ensure trusses are fully supported during fixing, are strapped to
  wall-plates and gables and are fully braced against wind
Consider the lifting of complete roofs when a crane is available, since
  accurate assembly is easier at ground level.

Timber: purlin and beam
Note general points made about trussed rafter construction and that purlins
  and purlin beams are less susceptible to damage during handling
Crane handling of longer span units is necessary
Levelling and bedding on walls is critical: setting out of purlins is often easiest
  from eaves level; padstones allow horizontal adjustment
Stress graded timber should be used for rafters
In storage, the protection of timber components against extremes of dry or
  wet conditions is essential
Strap, tie and fix components correctly.

Timber joisted: flat or low pitched
Correct stress grading of structural timbers is essential
In storage, protect timber against weather; control moisture content in
  particular
Space and level joists accurately and tie in to main structure with mild steel
  straps and timber packings
Provide sufficient bridging and strutting over longer spans
Ventilate 'cold' roof spaces; do not ventilate warm or 'inverted' roofs *(6.23)*
Fix decking to adequate falls; specify sheet materials correctly, using
  interlocking sheets and glueing joints as well as screwing and nailing.

Steel: lattice beam

Many of the points made about steel frame construction apply also to lattice beams.

These include:

- the desirability of variety reduction in beam lengths and node conditions (6.22)
- the importance of accurate setting out and levelling, affected by the accuracy of the frame and sub-structure
- use of adequately skilled labour and supervision
- use of the correct plant
- choice of the most appropriate jointing and fixing systems
- minimum time in storage: beams should be fixed direct from the delivery vehicle if possible

In addition, site assembly of larger beams may be necessary

Protect beams against damage and corrosion

Consider location and fixing of secondary structures, such as purlins, sheeting rails and structural decking; consider requirements of the cladding system chosen.

Steel: portal frames

Many of the points made for lattice beams apply to portals. In particular:

Accurate site assembly is necessary and to this end, foundation preparation is important

Portal sections must be handled by crane

Jointing technique should be considered

Consider the requirements, especially the accurate plumbing and lining through of the completed structure.

Steel: other types

Large size may mean more problems with site assembly, owing to the greater number of components

Crane handling and lifting of sub-assemblies will be a major factor

The use of site welding should be minimised

Consider the requirements of secondary structures, including glazing systems, especially accurate plumbing and lining through

Consider the needs of roof-mounted services such as ducting, trunking and lighting.

Concrete: in situ: slab and beam

Many of the points made about concrete floors apply also to concrete roofs.

These include:

- concrete quality
- testing
- formwork
- reinforcement

Consider drying out in relation to roof finishes; consider use of warm or 'inverted' roof construction and of lightweight screeds

Quality of labour and supervision are especially important

Shuttering and formwork: the support for this can cause problems for work
proceeding below, owing to the need for props, unless 'flying' shutters are
used
Consider services distribution.

Concrete: precast
See also section on precast concrete floors (xi), since many of the same points
apply.
In particular:
Additional in situ topping may be needed for fire resistance
Bay design should be modular to reduce the need for extra in situ work
Consider services, especially where units are prestressed.

References
[53]BRE/DoE, *Pitched roofs : trussed rafters – site storage : DAS 5, BRE*
[54]*BRE/DoE, Pitched roofs : trussed rafters – installation of bracing and binders*, DAS 24, BRE
[55]TRADA, *Roofs*, 51/6, TRADA
[56]International Truss Plate Association, *Technical bulletins and information sheets* (various), ITPA
[57]Tarmac/RIBA, *Flat roofing : a guide to good practice*, RIBA 1982
[58]BRE, *Flat roof design: the technical options*, Digest 221, HMSO
[59]Blackledge, G F, *Man on the job* (MoJ) leaflets, Nos. 1–18, C & CA

(xiii) Superstructures: claddings The following claddings will be considered as being typical of modern construction:
Masonry Brick and block
Timber Profiled; panels
Concrete Precast; grc
Composite Steel profiled; plastics coated; sandwich.

Masonry: brick and block[60] Infill panels have already been discussed, also brick claddings to timber framed structures (see (vii) (viii)). A major problem identified was differential movement between frame and panel, necessitating careful attention to tolerances[61]. The construction of masonry (brick) cladding to timber frame structures is made easier by having the template of the frame to work to, but care must be taken to tie the brickwork back to the frame using wall-ties at correct spacings. Ties should be fixed securely through the sheathing to the studs; this is easier if the stud positions are clearly marked on the sheating or breather paper.

Block claddings can be either left fair-faced or rendered, although problems of drying shrinkage and separation of render from backing can occur. Blocks can be delivered in shrink-wrapped packs, like bricks, and, especially if fair-faced, must be carefully handled and stored prior to laying. Laying of fair-faced blocks requires extra skill owing to the size of the units, making it harder to correct errors in jointing. Block thicknesses have tended to increase to meet insulation requirements, which can cause difficulty in handling, especially at shoulder height *(6.30)*. This factor should be taken

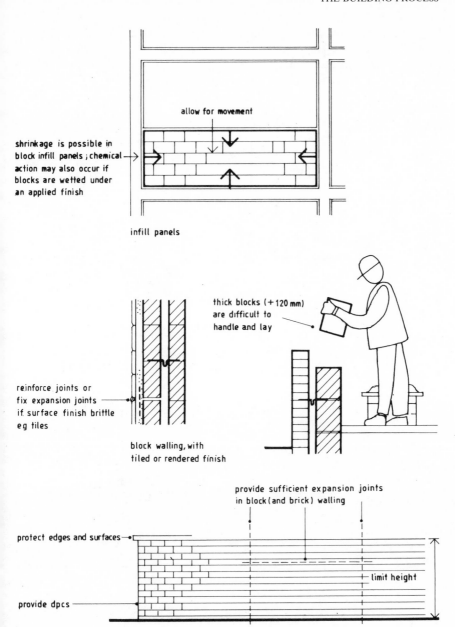

allow for movement

shrinkage is possible in block infill panels; chemical action may also occur if blocks are wetted under an applied finish

infill panels

thick blocks (+120 mm) are difficult to handle and lay

reinforce joints or fix expansion joints if surface finish brittle eg tiles

block walling, with tiled or rendered finish

provide sufficient expansion joints in block (and brick) walling

protect edges and surfaces

limit height

provide dpcs

6.30 *Blockwork: quality factors*

into account by designers. Different mortars may be needed for inner and outer leaves[62], leading to complications in mix specification and control; pre-mixed mortars may be desirable in these circumstances. In the case of rendering, other trades, usually plasterers, will be involved and, because this work takes place relatively late in the building sequence, scaffolding may have to be retained for uneconomic periods of time.

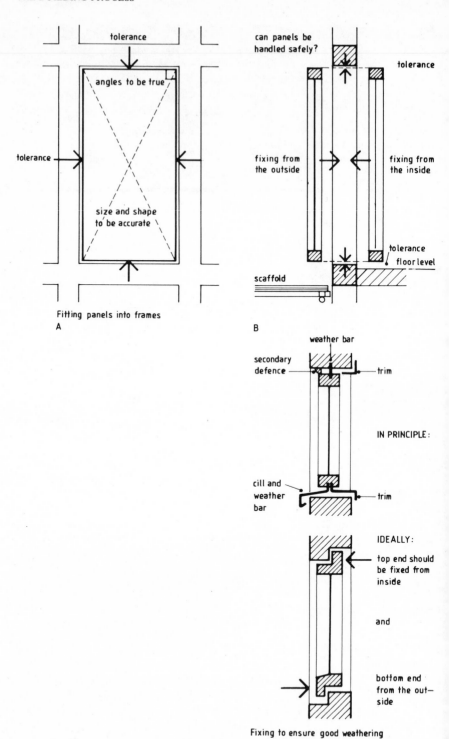

Fitting panels into frames
A

B

Fixing to ensure good weathering

6.31   *Infill panels: fixing problems; designing for assembly*

94

Most bricks suffer less than blocks from drying shrinkage, but may be prone to the leaching out of soluble salts and show efflorescence in exposed locations. Cavities should be properly drained and skins tied back securely to frames and sub-strates. Tile and brick slip finishes can suffer from differential movement of frame and cladding, which can cause buckling and separation from the backing (6.18). To reduce this risk, the mix and consistency of bedding compounds must be carefully controlled and mechanical fixings provided if in doubt. Expansion joints are necessary on long runs of cladding, for example every 12 m in brickwork, filled with compressible material and pointed with non-setting mastic.

In general, quality on site is improved if variety reduction is observed; if complex cladding details are avoided, especially round frames and at interfaces with different materials (6.31); if sequencing of work is studied; and if finishes can be applied shortly after the cladding is completed, rather than much later in the job.

Timber claddings: profiled boarding: infill panels[63] Boarding may be worked to different sectional profiles, such as shiplap and v-jointed, and fixed as cladding to treated softwood battens, which are themselves fixed to the backing material; this is often concrete or clinker block. Two trades are involved with this work, with a third, decorator, required later in the job (6.32). Timber must be selected and stored correctly, under cover on racks, and allowed to acquire the right moisture content before fixing. Fixing should be by means of non-ferrous screws or nails. Good access to the work is necessary and the backing sub-strate should have been completed and dried out before work commences. Damage to the timber must be avoided. End junctions between lengths of timber must be neatly executed, with corners mitred or protected with metal or plastic trim. Sufficient fixings must be used to prevent movement in the timber (6.33).

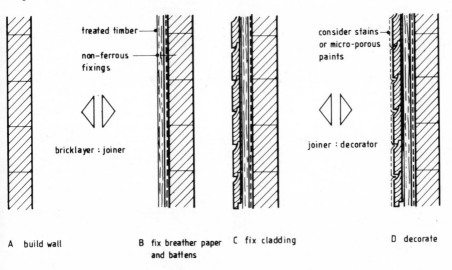

treated timber

non-ferrous fixings

bricklayer : joiner

consider stains or micro-porous paints

joiner : decorator

A build wall

B fix breather paper and battens

C fix cladding

D decorate

6.32 *Timber claddings: building sequence/trade interfaces*

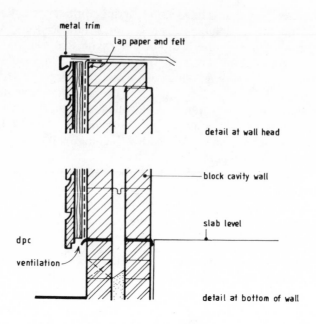

metal trim

lap paper and felt

detail at wall head

block cavity wall

slab level

dpc

ventilation

detail at bottom of wall

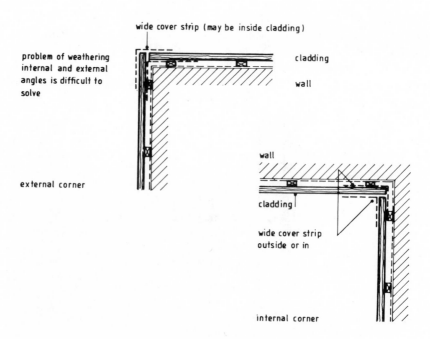

wide cover strip (may be inside cladding)

problem of weathering internal and external angles is difficult to solve

cladding

wall

external corner

wall

cladding

wide cover strip outside or in

internal corner

6.33 *Timber claddings: edges and angles*

96

Infill panels consist of timber-based sheets, such as plywood, fixed into soft or hardwood frames. The complete frame is then fixed to a secondary structure of timber posts, beams and noggings. Other types of sub-structure are possible. A layer of insulation is fixed behind the panel, together with a vapour check and some system of lining. Essentially, the problems are those of moisture resistance, thermal control and durability of the panel materials. These are created in turn by the jointing systems and the need for effective weathering. Workmanship must be excellent to ensure adequate durability; for this reason, designers must fully understand the physics of moisture migration and thermal performance and specify materials and assemblies accordingly (6.34).

The assembly of most sandwich infill panels will be carried out in the shop. Panels will then be brought to site and manhandled or craned into position. Handling should respect the fact that all timber components are usually weak in the plane at right angles to that of the panel. There is also a risk of damage through 'racking', in which the panels are pushed out of square. Tolerances between a panel and its neighbour in the framing system should be carefully observed (6.31). Joints should be made mechanically, rather than with glues or mastics. Decoration will often be required later in the job, for which access must be provided, and maintenance costs can be high.

Concrete panels: precast; grc[64,65,66] These are fixed to framed structures, commonly precast or in situ concrete; the glass reinforcement mats give grc panels good strength to weight ratios. Panels are cast in the factory and delivered to site by lorry. Handling of panels must be carried out correctly to avoid impact damage during lifting and stress reversals resulting from lifting at the wrong points. Panels should be clearly coded and marked in the casting yard before delivery to ensure they are off-loaded in the correct order for fixing. Measurements should be checked against complete frame dimensions and fixings must allow tolerances for dimensional error in both frame and panel (6.31). Storage of panels on site should be minimised: there will be financial on-costs involved, space will be taken up by panels awaiting fixing and double-handling will be necessary. On the other hand, fixing directly from the lorry can delay turn-round of the vehicle, unless a system of 'tugs' and trailers is used. After arrival on site, all panels should be checked for size and accuracy and for any damage, unacceptable panels being returned.

Lifting and fixing of panels requires expert control of the crane, with accurate directions from the banksman. Location and seating must be carefully prepared before placing. This may involve the fixing of levelling bolts, the laying of concrete bedding and the pre-location of steel brackets. Fixing of continuity steel may be necessary immediately after placing, together with grouting of beds and joints and the fixing of weather-resistant strips, seals and gaskets. Care with this part of the work is particularly important. Note that a number of different skills are needed during this process: specialist erectors, often sub-contracted, labourers, concretors, steel fixers and a variety of different equipment, varying from cranes to hand tools and specialised equipment. In addition to fixing the panels themselves,

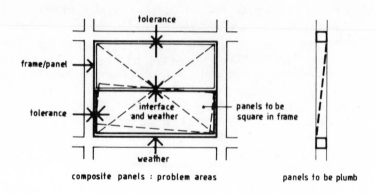

composite panels : problem areas   panels to be plumb

panels to be 'square' on plan

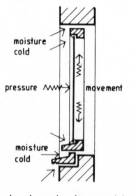

glazed panels : danger points

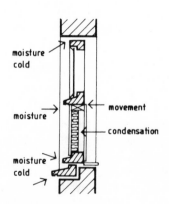

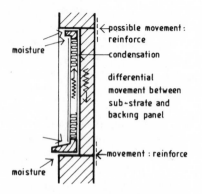

6.34 *Composite and sandwich panels: problem areas*

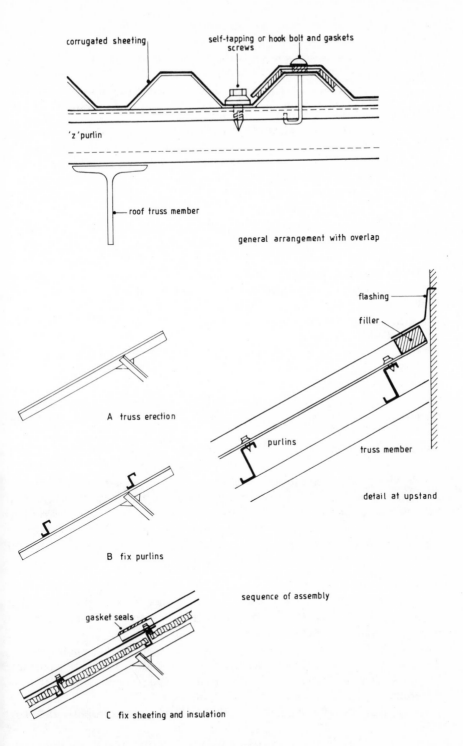

corrugated sheeting

self-tapping or hook bolt and gaskets
screws

'z' purlin

roof truss member

general arrangement with overlap

flashing

filler

purlins

truss member

detail at upstand

A truss erection

B fix purlins

sequence of assembly

gasket seals

C fix sheeting and insulation

6.35   *Fixing steel and composite corrugated roofing*

concrete for bedding must be mixed, lifted and placed, also possibly reinforcement and weathering materials.

Grc panels[67], because lighter in weight than concrete precast ones, can be handled using lighter equipment and more can be carried on each delivery vehicle. Because of their construction, however, generous allowance must be made for thermal movement in the fixings and supporting frame.

Composite: steel profiled: plastics coated   Applications are usually industrial, where large surfaces have to be covered quickly. Profiled sheeting may be used on both roofs and walls. Protection against damage to lower walls, both inside and out, is often necessary, using more durable claddings such as masonry, or by providing 'crash bars'. Internal linings, including insulation, are now required by Regulation[68].

Sheets and panels are secured to the primary or secondary structural system either by using bolts fixed with nuts and compressible sealing washers or shanked pins and self-tapping screws (6.35). Compressible gaskets are fitted between the sheets at overlaps and filler pieces are used at ridges, verges and upstands. Sheets are manufactured in the factory and delivered to the site in packs. Storage of packs in a secure area may be necessary prior to fixing. Crane handling of batches of sheeting to roof level is necessary, together with all necessary gaskets and fixings.

Fixing is carried out by specialist erectors, with attendance provided by the general contractor's own men. Where operatives have been properly trained, fixing is a simple procedure where areas are uninterrupted. Designers should, however, consider sheeting modules and the difficulty of forming upstands, glazed areas, overhangs, and similar details (6.36). After completion of the weatherproof skin, internal linings are fixed. These usually consist of insulation boards fixed to the purlins and other structural members, with a further skin of some finishing material. It is often possible to use sandwich panels which meet the requirements for both insulation and finishing. Should steel panels be damaged during fixing, damaged areas must be touched up with rust-proofing compound to prevent corrosion. For the same reason, panel fixings must be coated or non-ferrous. Services may be incorporated within the thickness of the panels but, where this is done, access for maintenance and replacement must be provided.

Composite: sandwich panels   These comprise a range of flat sheet materials fixed inside a frame. Typical examples are panels faced with glazed and vitreous enamelled sheets. Construction of these panels is complex in that there are many joints between the infill sheet and the frame, any of which can allow water to enter unless properly formed. There are further joints between the complete panel and the backing materials and surrounding structure. There is also the problem of condensation and unseen degradation of materials occurring within the panel thickness (6.34).

Panels must be manufactured off-site, with all joints properly detailed, fixed and sealed to minimise entry of water and to resist subsequent degradation. Careful handling, preferably in the vertical plane, is necessary to prevent undue stressing of joints through twisting or racking. Storage must also minimise stress in panels, by ensuring that they are properly supported and protected. Fixing requires equal care, especially if the panels contain glass or other brittle materials. Allowance should be made for the fixing of internal linings and finishes. Fixing teams should be experienced in this type of work, which again may be a specialist and sub-contracted item.

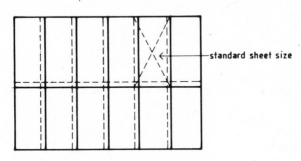

roof plan : simple modular arrangement of sheeting

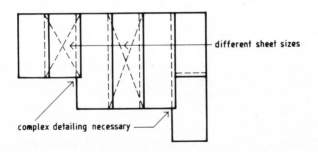

complex arrangement of sheeting

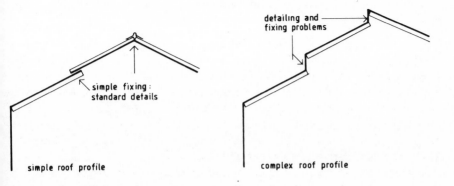

6.36 *Variety reduction in steel and composite roofs*

Summary of points affecting cladding panels

Masonry
Consider modules and tolerances
Fix back securely to the superstructure
Allow for thermal and moisture movement, especially in blockwork
Allow extra care when laying fairface blocks
Ensure blocks can be handled easily
Note that mortar mixes may vary between inner and outer skins
Consider rendering problems: backing, shrinkage, and late application, leading to problems of work sequencing
Allow for differential movement, especially with brick and tile slips
Provide expansion joints at recommended intervals
Avoid complex details, especially at junctions, which can increase the risk of failure.

Timber
Selection and storage of timber is important
Consider trade interfaces; backing, cladding and decorating require joiners, bricklayers and decorators
Sub-strates and backings should be at the correct moisture contents before fixing
Battens and all concealed timber should be treated against rot
Fixings to be non-ferrous or coated
Avoid damage during handling and fixing
Consider junctions and corners: design to minimise rot in end-grain and provide sufficient fixings
Note that many joints in infill panels can allow water to enter, leading to problems of moisture and thermal movement, durability and maintenance; workmanship must be to a high standard; panels are weak normal to their surface planes and must be carried with care to minimise twist and racking
Consider tolerances between panels and the surrounding structure; use 'mechanical' joints where possible
If decoration is required, note that maintenance costs can be high.

Concrete: precast; grc
Handle carefully to avoid impact damage and stress reversal: use correct lifting points
Mark panels clearly and deliver in order of fixing
Minimise storage on site; fix direct from the lorry, unless turn-round must be rapid, to obviate this problem; consider the use of trailers
Check panels for size and accuracy upon arrival on site
Prepare panel location points, reinforcements, fixing brackets, bedding
Level panels accurately after placing
Fix reinforcement; pack and grout joints fully using the correct mix
Ensure skill and equipment levels are appropriate for the job; provide adequate supervision

Grc panels are light and therefore easier to handle; make generous allowance for movement in both panels and frame.

Composite: profiled: plastics coated
Avoid use on lower walls, where protection against damage may be needed
Avoid damage to sheets during transit and fixing since this may result in corrosion
Touch up any damaged areas
Ensure correct spacing and location of fixings; use compressible gaskets and washers
Consider sheeting modules; avoid difficult details, such as upstands and overhangs
Reduce the variety of different finishes
Fix insulation and linings correctly
Design to minimise risk of condensation
Allow for services to be incorporated within the thickness of the panel.

Composite: sandwich panels
Remember that infill sheeting may contain brittle materials: great care in storage and handling is then essential
Detail all joints properly: consider joints both within the panel and between the panel and supporting sub-structure or framework
Handle panels carefully to minimise stress in the joints
Where retro-fitting of insulation and linings is necessary, consider trade sequences and interfaces.

References
[60]BDA, *Brickwork cladding to multi-storey reinforced concrete framed structures*, TN9, BDA, 1975
[61]BRE, *Getting good fit*, Digest 199, HMSO
[62]BRE, *Mortars for bricklaying*, Digest 160, HMSO
[63]TRADA, *External timber cladding*, Wood Information Sheet 1–20, TRADA
[64]Oram, W R, *Precast concrete cladding*, C & CA
[65]BRE, *GRC*, Digest 216, HMSO
[66]BRE, *Fixings for non-loadbearing precast concrete cladding panels*, Digest 235, HMSO
[67]BRE, *GRC*, Digest 216, HMSO
[68]*The Building Regulations*, (1st Amendment Regulations 1978), Part FF, HMSO

(xiv) Roof finishes: tiles and slates; felts; poured types
Tiles and slates   These are laid on and fixed to timber battens over sarking felt, or sometimes over boarding or sheeting. Tiles may be coloured concrete or natural clay and slates either the natural material, which is expensive, or made from artificial substances. Materials are delivered in packs and stored in the open; care should be taken therefore to protect them from damage. Tiles and slates are lifted in batches to roof level where they are rested on the battens ready for fixing. Lifting can be either manual or by fixed hoist or mobile plant.

Sarking felt[69] is supplied in rolls. During fixing, there is a risk of puncturing the material. It must be laid over the rafters from the eaves upwards and parallel to the eaves; sufficient overlap should be allowed between sheets.

Battens consist of softwood, impregnated against rot. Timber must be properly stored and protected from the weather on covered racks. Spacing of fixings should be at the correct gauge for the tiles or slates being used. Tiles and slates are fixed with non-ferrous nails and clips as required by the manufacturers. Ridges, verges and undercloaks should be bedded and pointed in dense mortar; with roll tiles, proprietary infill units may be used.

Felts and membranes[70]   These are laid on flat roofs. Sub-strates may be boarding, sheet materials, screeds or composites. Quality in flat roof fixing depends upon the correct laying and forming both of the sub-strates and of the felts themselves. Sub-strates should be properly bonded or mechanically fixed to the supporting structure and have a flush upper surface. It is essential to allow for movement of the substrate or to protect the membrane from undue movement by laying insulation and other materials over it (inverted roof) *(6.23)*. Substrates should be laid to adequate and even falls to prevent collection of water on the roof surface. Felts and membranes are laid in widths, either by bedding on hot bitumen, or by 'torching on'. The separate layers are laid so that joints do not coincide. Edge detailing of the roof is important and must be carried out carefully. The felt, once laid, must be protected against rapid changes in temperature by the provision of a reflective surface. It may sometimes be necessary to ventilate a felted roof to ensure substrate temperatures are controlled and thermal creep reduced. Rainwater outlets should be set at the correct levels and positioned so as to get the water off the roof quickly. Roofs should be designed that are simple in form on plan, that avoid complex upstands, and that minimise penetration through the roof by pipes, ducts and other services *(6.37)*. During laying, care must be taken to avoid damaging the substrate materials, especially insulation, and to prevent water from being trapped in the roof. In particular, sufficient time should be allowed for underlying structures to dry out. Laying felt and plastics membranes (use of the latter can reduce the number of laying operations) is usually a sub-contracted item.

Asphalts[70]   Laid on flat roofs and floors, asphalts are used where heavier traffic is expected than with felted roofs. Substrates are usually heavier than with felts, for example concrete slabs. They may consist of pre-formed slabs, such as wood-wool. Substrates must be rigid, since asphalt will accommodate only limited movement. A membrane, such as felt, must be laid below the asphalt to allow for thermal movement. Special plant is required to heat the asphalt, which is then lifted to roof level or, in the case of floors, carried into the building and poured. After pouring, the asphalt is ironed flat and allowed to set. Two-coat work is usual for ordinary roofs. The finished surface should be protected with a reflective coating. Labour is specialised for this work, which is normally a sub-contract item.

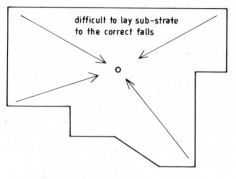

complex and simple roof forms

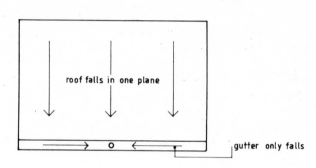

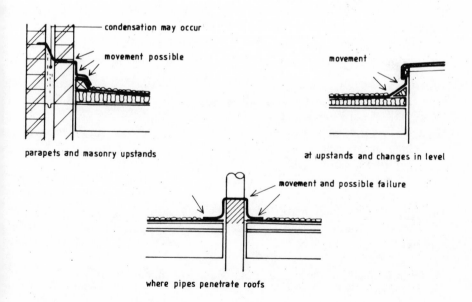

6.37 *Flat roofs: problem areas*

Summary of quality factors:
Tiles and slates
Off-load onto a hard standing, away from site traffic
Handle carefully to minimise risk of breakage
Lift to roof manually or with hoist or mobile plant
Avoid puncturing sarking felt during laying
Lay correctly, parallel to the eaves; allow proper overlaps
Ensure battens are stored correctly on racks and treated against rot before
    fixing
Bed, point and fill undercloaks, verges and ridges; use proprietary filler units
    where appropriate
Fix with non-ferrous or coated nails and clips.

Felts and membranes
Lay or form substrates correctly: cover joints and minimise flexing by
    providing enough supports
Allow for any movement of the substrate by protecting against extremes of
    temperature
Protect the waterproof membrane by providing a reflective surface
Lay substrates to adequate and even falls
Rainwater channels and outlets to be to even falls and fixed at levels which
    will ensure water is discharged from the roof surface quickly
Avoid coincident joints in felt layers
Detail edges correctly
Ventilate felts where necessary
Avoid complex roof forms and penetration of roof surfaces by pipes, flues
    and changes in level
Take care during laying to avoid damaging either the felt or the substrate
Ensure operatives are properly skilled and that supervision is adequate.

Asphalts
Lay or form substrates correctly; allow for any movement in the substrate,
    especially where this is of concrete construction
Ensure structural bays are rigid and provide movement joints to avoid
    cracking of the asphalt
Lay separating membrane below the asphalt
Ensure special plant can be brought close to the building and that hoists
    and/or ramps are provided
Allow each coat to set before laying the next and, in the case of floors,
    programme for nil or limited access to the building during the setting
    period
Protect finished surfaces
Ensure labour skill levels are adequate and allow management resource for a
    sub-contract item.

References
[69]BRE/DoE *Pitched roofs : sarking felt underlay – watertightness*, DAS 10, BRE
[70]BRE, *Asphalt and built-up felt roofing : durability*, Digest 144, HMSO

(xv) Finishes and fittings: partitions

Partitions: masonry[71]   Most internal masonry partitions are built from blockwork. Load-bearing partitions may be built in high strength blocks or brickwork. Block partitions in ground floors are usually built at the same time as the external and separating walls, to avoid return visits by the bricklayers. Thin, light-weight blocks are often used on upper floors, since they are easier to fix into than timber studwork. A disadvantage of this practice is that 'wet' work is brought back on site at what should be a 'dry' stage of construction, although this may not matter if the walls are to be plastered.

Quality factors with block partitions include:

Proper setting out: partition lines should be clearly indicated on the floor, also the positions of openings

Floor to ceiling dimensions should be established which minimise the cutting of blocks, enabling full courses to be used without the need for cut blocks or coursing bricks *(6.16)*

Accurate forming of openings is necessary to ensure that timber door frames or casings will fit; proper levelling and bedding of lintels, with allowance for settlement, is vital

Tying in the partitions to external walls, either by block-bonding or with metal ties or reinforcement, is essential to resist movement and cracking of finishes

Allowance should be made for block movement and shrinkage during drying out: this is especially important when walls are to be plastered; expansion joints should be provided where necessary

Surfaces should be keyed where necessary to ensure a good bond for plaster;

Chasing for service runs should be avoided wherever possible, but, where essential, locations and dimensions should be shown clearly on drawings *(6.40)*;

Other points concerning the handling and storage of blocks, appropriate mortar mixes, etc. are covered in Section (vii).

Partitions: timber stud[72]   A common form of partition in low-rise construction where there is a minimal requirement for acoustic or fire resisting separation between rooms, where the main structure is timber, as in 'platform frame' dwellings, and where weight-saving is important. Where partitions are made up on site, construction is similar to balloon-frame technique, but where they are supplied as part of a 'kit', it follows 'panel' principles, in which sections of completed partition are erected and nailed together. Erection requires relatively skilled work by the joiners when partitions are built on site from scratch, following the sequence of marking out, fixing head, sole and wall plates, and fixing studs and noggings *(6.38)*.

Quality factors include:

Ensure correct storage and selection of timber: moisture contents should be less than 20% before lining in; no twisted or bowed members should be used; treat timber in contact with ground floor slabs against rot;

Mark head and sole plates accurately to ensure partitions are plumb;

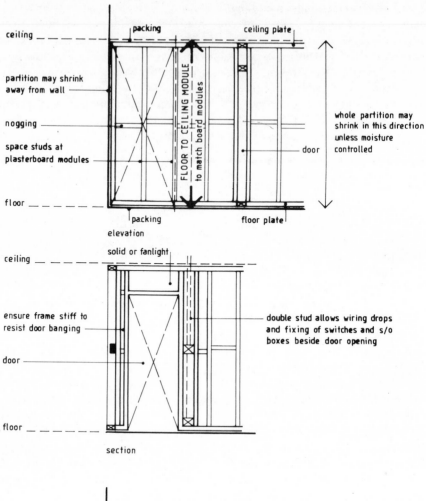

ceiling

packing

ceiling plate

partition may shrink away from wall

nogging

space studs at plasterboard modules

FLOOR TO CEILING MODULE
to match board modules

door

whole partition may shrink in this direction unless moisture controlled

floor

packing

floor plate

elevation

ceiling

solid or fanlight

ensure frame stiff to resist door banging

double stud allows wiring drops and fixing of switches and s/o boxes beside door opening

door

floor

section

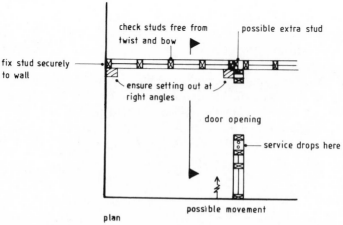

check studs free from twist and bow

possible extra stud

fix stud securely to wall

ensure setting out at right angles

door opening

service drops here

possible movement

plan

6.38 *Stud partitions: problem areas*

108

Ensure accurate cutting of housings, mortices, tenons and bridles; cut members to the correct length;

Ensure proper fixing (usually by skew nailing);

Provide sufficient noggings, bearers and supports for wall-mounted fittings;

Ensure accurate forming of openings to ensure frames and casings will fit; consider tolerances;

Allow for forming service ducts and runs, for example by the provision of double studs beside door openings *(6.38)*;

Other points concerning timber construction are covered in Sections 6(c) and 6(d) (viii).

Partitions: proprietary These include hollow-cored, plaster-board-faced and framed and panelled systems[73].

With the former, the frames are supplied in room-height sections, similar to plasterboard sheets, and are cut and fitted using softwood wall and floor plates to locate and stiffen the panels. The latter are made in a variety of proprietary framing and infill types and patterns, the frames usually being formed in metal, with the infill panels glazed or solid; panels have various finishes. These systems are most used in commercial buildings, owing to the quality of finish which can be achieved and because most systems are demountable and re-usable, allowing flexibility in planning *(6.39)*.

Quality points on proprietary systems:
Hollow-cored plasterboard partitions

Supplied and handled as plasterboards: easily damaged by rough handling; protect against this and against excessive absorption of moisture *(6.04)*

Store correctly: consider delivery direct to the work-place for temporary storage prior to fixing; panels should be stored flat

Fixing by joiners or plasterers: Joiners may be preferable, owing to the need to fix timber plates, junction pieces, frames and bearers; the decision is affected by trade practice, however, in addition to availability of particular trades, skill levels and costs

Ensure accurate marking of lines of head and sole-plates and that partitions are erected plumb

Cut panels accurately, using sharp tools

Assemble by seating panels on timber plates; avoid undue hammering, which can damage both cores and panel edges

Form openings for doors, etc, accurately and allow correct tolerances to permit fitting of door frames and casings

Avoid having to drive in bearers to cores for wall-mounted fittings by locating the bearers prior to erecting partitions

Allow for services to be incorporated without rough and unsightly cutting of panels, by pre-forming ducts, holes and accesses.

Proprietary frame and panel type partitions (6.39)

Usually supplied and handled as specialist items; easily damaged by rough handling; protect by storing correctly and delaying delivery until needed

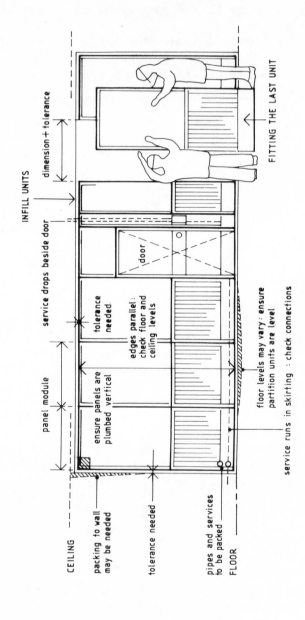

CEILING

packing to wall
may be needed

panel module

tolerance needed

ensure panels are
plumbed vertical

tolerance
needed

edges parallel:
check floor and
ceiling levels

service drops beside door

INFILL UNITS

dimension + tolerance

FITTING THE LAST UNIT

door

floor levels may vary: ensure
partition units are level

service runs in skirting : check connections

pipes and services
to be packed

FLOOR

6.39 *Proprietary partitions: problem areas*

Fixing is usually a specialist, sub-contract item; ensure management and
   programming allows for this
Since frames and panels are usually made up off site, accurate dimensions
   must be supplied to the manufacturers
Floors and ceilings must be level: allow for variation in surfaces and out of
   square corners
Fix in the correct sequence, according to manufacturer's instructions: usually
   the frame, followed by solid panels, followed by glazing
Ensure that openings are correctly located and accurate; provide for service
   runs, holes for pipes, etc
Design in bearers for wall-mounted fittings
Protect against damage caused by following trades.

References
[71]Tovey, A K, *Concrete masonry for the contractor*, C & CA
[72]TRADA, *Internal walls and partitions*, IBL 51/3, TRADA
[73]British Gypsum, *British Gypsum White Book*, 5th edition, British Gypsum 1984

(xvi) Finishes and fittings: 'First Fix'

General This comprises all the work which must be carried out to the
building before the application of wall, ceiling and floor finishes.

The quality of the completed building is decided for most clients by the
quality of finishes and fittings and roughly 50% of the cost of the building is
accounted for by this stage of the work. Poor quality in the sub-structures and
super-structures of the building may lead to catastrophic and expensive
failure: work *has* to be right during these stages, therefore, since such failure
is hard to correct. Poor quality work during the finishing stages will probably
be evident sooner than structural failure, since this work is immediately
visible. Fortunately, it is usually easier to correct, unless the underlying
structure is either the cause of the failure or has itself been affected by it.
Underpinning quality during the finishing stages is the quality of work during
'First Fix', since this provides both the framework and the basis for the
finishes themselves. It includes roughing-in and carcassing work by, mainly,
joiners, electricians and plumbers. The work of these trades will be dealt with
in turn.

Joinery Joiner's work includes fitting staircases, forming ducts, fixing
bearers and battens, fixing skirting grounds, door linings and frames and
generally preparing the way for the other trades working at this stage – mainly
electricians and plumbers – and for the following trades of plasterers and dry
liners *(6.40)*. As mentioned above, the joiners often erect proprietary
partitions, in addition to those made from timber studwork.

Quality factors to be observed by joiners include:
Accurate location, measurement and setting out of all work: this is
   fundamental, since otherwise panels, frames, sheets and components will
   not fit
Sequence of work: this affects especially partitions, staircases, sanitary and
   other plumbing items and some floor finishes, such as screeds

111

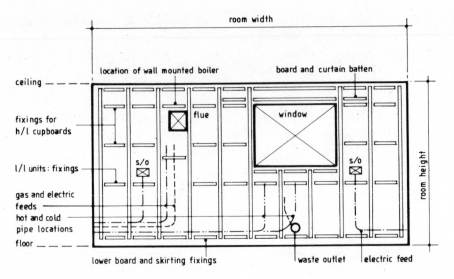

elevation of typical kitchen wall

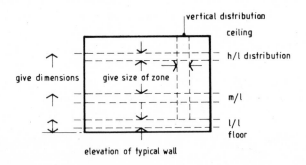

elevation of typical wall

'ZONING' system for services

6.40   *First Fix: locations of fixings and services*

Timbers should be correctly stored at the correct moisture content and
   handled and pre-treated against rot where in contact with a damp
   substrate; fixings should be non-ferrous under the same conditions of use
Staircases are often not fitted until later in the job since there is a risk of
   damage, in which case temporary vertical access will be necessary and
   openings in floors will have to be protected by guard rails.

Electrical[74]   Electrician's work during 'First Fix' includes the fixing of the
consumer control unit, busbars and conduit and of wiring in ducts and chases
provided by preceding trades. They are dependent upon assistance from
other trades working alongside them in the building, especially joiners
erecting partitions and forming ducts, and plumbers fixing pipework and
fittings. Since electrical services are routed through other components, the
question of who forms access panels, notches, holes, chases and ducts must be

decided. The architect can help by so designing the building that these 'enabling' routes can be formed and installation made easily, for example by incorporating double studs beside door openings for wiring drops and by considering economical ways of routeing conduit and wiring across joists and beams, perhaps by using de-mountable skirtings *(6.41)*. Quality can suffer badly if electricians form their own routes by random drilling through joists and partitions or by chasing across screeds and down walls, without due regard for following trades.

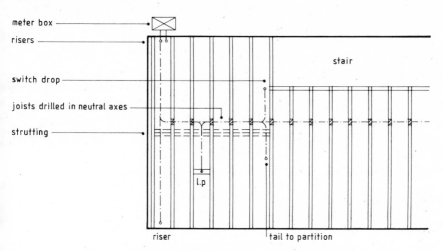

plan of 1st floor joists showing wiring routes

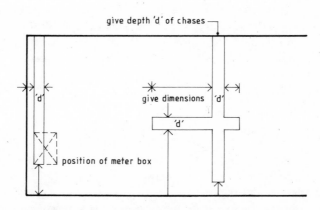

elevation of typical wall showing location of any chases and ducts required

6.41   *Electrical First Fix: wiring routes, ducts and chases*

In summary the following quality points should be observed:

Establish clearly preferred routes for all distribution systems and locate fixtures and fittings early in the design of the building

Design distribution routes and accesses and show these clearly on drawings. This should assist the work of the electrician, who is usually a sub-contractor working to a tight time scale and who has little time to plan layouts to suit other trades

Programme the work to allow for attendance if builder's work has to be done

Ensure minimum interference between trades working in the building at the same time, by avoiding locating all services in one area and by efficient programming

Difficulties in programming may be caused if electrical work is closely dependent upon the fixing of such items as lift machinery, ventilation plant and suspended ceilings which incorporate lighting units. Wherever possible, interference should be designed out or eliminated by effective management

Consider working space for electricians, especially in ducts and plant rooms

Consider ease of maintenance and replacement of electrical items

Ensure all equipment is tested before handover.

Plumbing[75]   Plumbers are dependent on joiners during 'First Fix' to fix bearers and sometimes to form openings; joiners will also, as with electrical work, provide attendance, by forming ducts, making cradles for baths and stillages to support tanks and cylinders and so on. The plumbers' work includes the provision of concealed pipework, in floor spaces and elsewhere, the fitting of tanks, cisterns and cyclinders and of soil and vent pipes and wastes *(6.42)*. The installation of fittings and most of the central heating is left until 'Second Fix' stage. Outside the shell, plumbers fix flashings and soakers, gutters and downpipes, lead slates and vent and overflow pipes, attending upon the roofers and carpenters during this process. Plumbing materials and jointing methods vary, which dictates both the attendance needed and the skill level required. Other work includes the installation of some fire protection systems, and the provision of any specialised items within the building.

Summary of quality points

Establish clearly preferred routes for all pipework, in relation to the location of fittings, early in the design of the building

Design routes and accesses for all pipework and ducting, where this is a plumber's item, and show these clearly on drawings

Programme the work in relation to that of roofers, carpenters and other specialised erectors

Ensure minimum interference between trades working in the building at the same time, by avoiding locating all services in one area and by efficient programming

Design to allow enough working space for plumbers, especially in bathrooms, WCs, service areas and ductwork

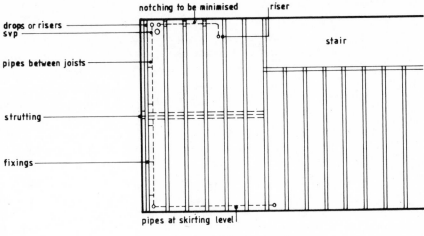

plan of 1st floor joists showing pipe runs

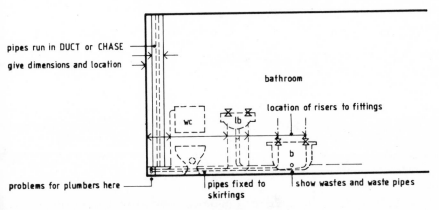

elevation of wall of typical bathroom

6.42   *Plumbing First Fix: pipe runs, ducts and chases*

Provide for access for subsequent maintenance and replacement
Ensure materials are of the right type and that fittings are compatible with
each other and properly stored;
Ensure components are undamaged before fixing, possibly by using kitted
systems
Ensure pipework is properly fixed and fully supported where necssary; drill
holes where pipes pass through walls
Test installations fully upon completion; ensure water, fuel and electrical
supplies are available for this purpose.

References
[74]Institute of Electrical Engineers, *Regulations for the electrical equipment of
buildings*, IEE, 1974
[75]*Local Water Authorities : Model Byelaws*

(xvii) Plastering and dry lining

Plastering[76-79] Plastering re-introduces wet work into the building process at a stage when the building is drying out. The reasons for plastering rather than for dry lining should therefore be carefully considered. With masonry construction, where there are block partitions, there is more justification for plastering than with timber frame and dry partitioning systems. Another factor is floor finishes: if floors are to be screeded anyway, another wet trade just preceding may not have a measurable effect upon drying-out time.

Plastering is normally sub-contracted and within the trade there are often sub-divisions into 'liners', 'plasterers' and 'ceiling fixers'. Management should recognise this and ensure a steady availability of surfaces ready for plastering to avoid many return visits and the complicated programming of sub-trades.

Work starts with the fixing of plasterboards to the ceilings. Walls are then 'floated', using one of several possible mixes, and ceilings are jointed. Once this work has set, walls and ceilings are skimmed or setting coats are applied; the timing of application of the setting coat will vary with the type of plaster.

A number of factors affect quality in plastering:

Plasterboards

Store in dry conditions, possibly in 'sets' for each building or 'space'

Handle carefully, especially across site; keep clean *(6.04) (6.05)*.

Background material and adhesion

Surfaces to be properly keyed

Surfaces with high or low suction require different treatments and sometimes a bonding agent may be necessary

Cementitious plasters are preferred in areas where there is a high risk of condensation

Setting out

Various techniques, using plumb lines, screeds, etc

Angles to be trued up and angle beads fixed

Grounds to be fixed where required; although less common now, the use of grounds is highly desirable to avoid the need for early fixing of finished joinery.

Mix

Knocked up within the building

Ensure use before 'going off'.

The problem of tolerances, levels, lines and plumbs can be a major factor in the quality of plastering work. Plasterers may have to correct poor tolerances worked to by bricklayers and, less usually, by carpenters, for example when fixing floor and ceiling joists *(6.43)*. Another factor is the tendency to fix some 'Second Fix' joinery, such as skirtings, before plastering: this practice may be followed where a delay between the application of backing and setting coats is necessary, but it should be avoided whenever possible: joinery can be damaged leading to shrinkage movement and fungal attack, and can absorb excess moisture *(6.44)*.

Plastering is closely interdependent with joinery, plumbing and other

116

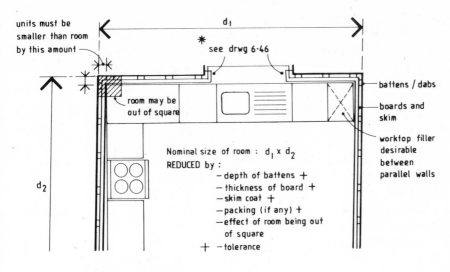

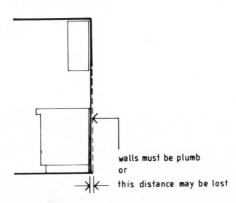

plan of part of kitchen

section through wall and units

6.43   *Plasterboarding and dry lining: effects on room dimensions*

services installations in traditional construction *(6.45)*. Joiners must attend
upon both plumbers and plasterers, who cannot complete their work until
grounds, partitions, duct framework, etc, have been fixed. This requires
careful management if continuity of work is to be maintained and quality is
not to suffer.

Dry lining[76,80]   This is an increasingly preferred system, since wet work is
largely eliminated *(6.46)*. Proprietary systems are available, including
complete partitioning systems (see (xv)). Walls are trued up and treated
battens are fixed, with packing if required; alternatively, plaster 'dab'
techniques may be used. Ceilings are boarded as with wet work. Once boards
have been fixed, they are jointed with tape and several layers of a special
plaster built up over the joint until a flush surface is achieved. Angles and
corners are taped and beaded, where surfaces are to be skimmed. Final finish
may be a thin skim coat (3 mm) or surfaces may be left ready for decoration.

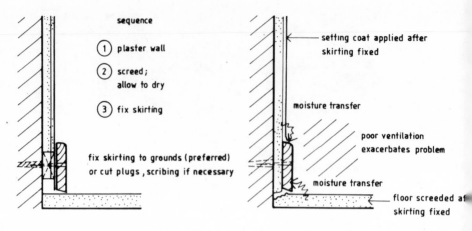

sequence

① plaster wall

② screed;
allow to dry

③ fix skirting

fix skirting to grounds (preferred)
or cut plugs, scribing if necessary

PREFERRED method

setting coat applied after
skirting fixed

moisture transfer

poor ventilation
exacerbates problem

moisture transfer

floor screeded af
skirting fixed

AVOID this method :
pre-fixing of skirtings to provide lines for
plasterers and screeders can cause mould
growth and rot in timber

6.44 *Fixing skirtings: plaster/screed interfaces*

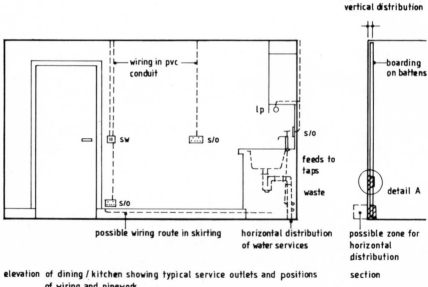

space available for
vertical distribution

wiring in pvc
conduit

lp

s/o

sw   s/o

boarding
on battens

feeds to
taps

waste

detail A

s/o

possible wiring route in skirting

horizontal distribution
of water services

possible zone for
horizontal
distribution

elevation of dining / kitchen showing typical service outlets and positions
of wiring and pipework

section

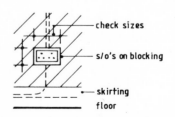

check sizes

s/o's on blocking

skirting

floor

detail plan showing fixing of pipes to battens

detail A forming openings in
boarding for outlets

6.45 *Plasterboarding: service runs and outlet points*

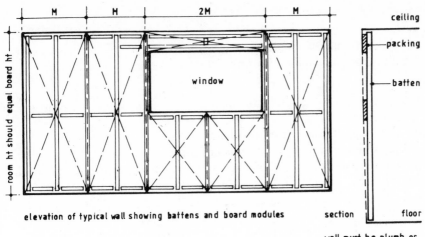

elevation of typical wall showing battens and board modules   section

wall must be plumb or
packing will be needed

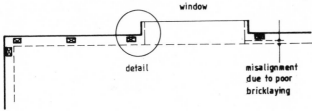

alignment of battens is essential

plan

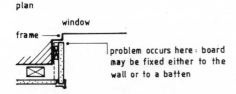

detail at window reveal

6.46   *Dry lining: setting out and fixing*

Quality factors in dry lining:
Battens and packing
Ensure only treated timber is used and that battens are plumb and surfaces
    level;
check accuracy, especially round openings

Dry lining boards
Store in dry conditions, possibly in sets for each building or 'space'; handle
    carefully, especially across site; keep clean

Fixing boards
Use correct, galvanised fixing nails
Do not damage surfaces where no skim will be applied

119

Do not fix too close to edges of boards

Jointing

Use correct plaster mix and ensure joints are smoothly taped: apply in layers
and build up gradually to form a flush surface; allow time to set

Skimming

Introduces wet work, but can provide a truer surface, given skilled
application
Use correct plaster mix and consistency
Special attention is needed to joints and angles
Do not skim over a resilient backing, such as insulating material, since
surfaces can crack when joinery is fixed after setting *(6.47)*.

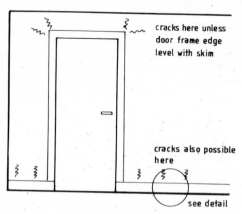

elevation showing areas of skim coat likely to crack

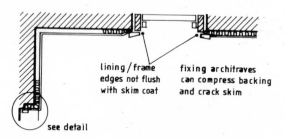

plan at door and window

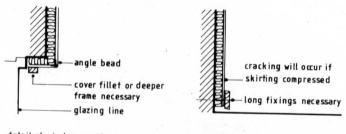

detail at window reveal   detail at skirting

6.47 *Plastering: problems with resilient backings*

Many of the points made under 'Plastering', with regard especially to tolerances, apply also to dry lining. Fixing of 'Second Fix' joinery is less critical with dry lining. A problem can occur where staircases are pre-fixed, requiring boards to be cut on the angle to match the rake of the string. If possible, boards should be fixed to walls before staircases are fitted. Designers should note that dry lining can alter room dimensions, especially if tolerances are incorrect: this can affect such items as kitchen units and bathroom wall tiling and change the spaces between units *(6.43)*. Dry lining is also interdependent with other trades, such as plumbing and electrical: conduit and some wiring and pipework must be installed before dry lining is carried out, and holes have to be cut in boards for outlet boxes and connections to fittings *(6.45)*. Some return visiting may be necessary to provide the attendance for this work.

Other points on plastering and dry lining: sufficient time should be allowed for buildings to dry out after the completion of plastering and screeding and before the fixing of many joinery items and the laying of floor tiles. This requirement can have a significant effect upon the time taken to complete the building.

References
[76]British Gypsum, *British Gypsum White Book*, 5th edition, British Gypsum 1984
[77]Taylor, J B, *Plastering*, Godwin
[78]BRE, *Choosing specifications for plastering*, Digest 213, HMSO
[79]DoE, *Plastering on building boards*, DoE Advisory leaflet No. 21, HMSO
[80]DoE, *Plasterboard dry linings*, DoE Advisory leaflet No. 64, HMSO

(xviii) Finishes and fittings: 'Second Fix'
General Once plastering or dry lining is finished, the previous trades return to the building to complete the fitting out. Even more than at 'First Fix' stage, the quality of the finished building will be dictated by the the care taken *(6.48)*. This implies practical and sensible design, a clear understanding by all tradesmen of the quality levels required and the availability of the right type and quality of labour, tools, materials and components. The achieveable quality will depend upon the quality of work done during the preceding stages. For example, if walls are not true or properly finished, the best finished fitting will not fit accurately; if radiators cannot be fixed because there are no battens, walls will be damaged while these are installed; if tolerances in the kitchen are wrong, the storage units may have to be chased into the plaster at each end and the wall tiles may have to be cut. 'Second Fix' includes the fitting of joinery, electrical and plumbing items, plus any specialist work on finishes.

Joinery Work at this stage can vary from the fitting of kitchen units *(6.49)*, bath panels, doors, aprons and staircase trim in dwellings, to the fitting of expensive wall lining and joinery units in offices. Joiners must work very closely with the other finishing trades, especially the plumbers and electricians and any specialist erectors engaged in fitting, for example, a suspended

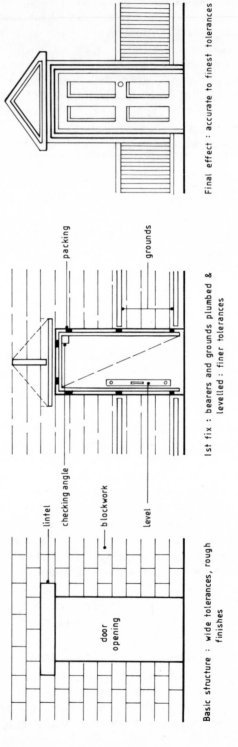

Final effect : accurate to finest tolerances

1st fix : bearers and grounds plumbed & levelled : finer tolerances

packing

grounds

Basic structure : wide tolerances, rough finishes

lintel

checking angle

blockwork

level

door opening

6.48 *Quality variation between sub-strates and finishes*

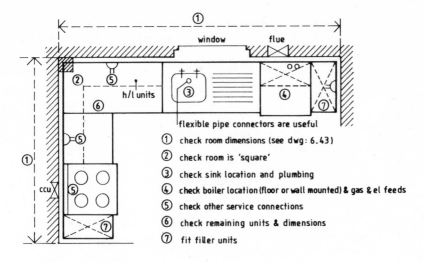

① check room dimensions (see dwg: 6.43)
② check room is 'square'
③ check sink location and plumbing
④ check boiler location (floor or wall mounted) & gas & el feeds
⑤ check other service connections
⑥ check remaining units & dimensions
⑦ fit filler units

plan of typical kitchen

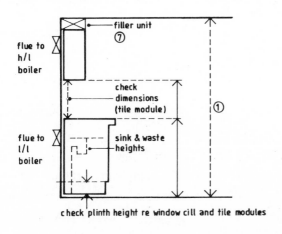

section through units

6.49   *Kitchen units: sequence of fitting and problem areas*

ceiling. Design must take account of the skill levels available and of the materials which will be used. For example, with routine housing work, newly trained operatives may be capable of fitting standard joinery sections in standard locations to an acceptable standard; for the executive office, however, only an experienced and highly trained craftsman may be capable of fitting mahogany wall panelling. Both clients and designers must be aware of the cost implications of these factors.

Quality factors to be observed by joiners include:
Selection of agreed quality levels for the finishes required
Practical and sensible design: can the work be carried out as designed? How
   long will it take to do it? What will it cost?

Selection of operatives with appropriate levels of skill

Selection of materials and components capable of being fixed by the operatives chosen

Accurate location, measurement and setting out of all items

Correct sequence of work and consideration of the interdependency between trades: for example, in the fitting of the bath and panel; in the installation of the kitchen sink

Correct storage and handling of timber: for example, it is especially important to ensure the right moisture content and undamaged materials

Use of correct fixings and fixing methods: materials should be compatible, for example by using brass screws in brass hinges; the importance of using the right tools for fixing.

Electrical[81]   The electrician's work at this stage is less dependent upon the accuracy of preceding trades, but is crucially dependent upon the quality of his own work during 'First Fix' and upon the attendance then given, especially by the joiners. For example, if switch and socket outlet boxes have not been properly located, set squarely on the wall and related vertically and horizontally to each other, nothing the electrician can do at this stage will improve matters: the cover plates will simply make the fittings look even more out of square. The designer can also have a major influence: for example, by designing the routes for wiring and conduit (6.41), by providing ducts and accesses for pipes and wiring, and by incorporating double studs beside door openings in stud partitions, he can ensure that the fittings are located where he wants them and that they will be related visually to the other elements in the room.

The electrician must also ensure that future maintenance of the installation is straightforward, for example, by providing good access to immersion heater bosses, and that the system is fully tested upon completion.

In summary

Check accuracy of the position of all socket outlets, switch and terminal boxes; ensure that they are set square in surfaces

Ensure fittings are correctly fixed in the mounting boxes

Ensure correct fittings are used

Check requirements of other trades: for example, ensure work relates to the programmes of any specialist erectors, such as those installing lighting and lift equipment

Programme work to ensure minimum interference with other trades

Designer to ensure that sufficiently durable fittings are chosen in relation to agreed quality levels, cost and skills of the tradesmen likely to be employed on the job

Electrician to attend upon other trades as required; installation to be fully tested upon completion; ensure power supplies are available for this purpose

Ensure future maintenance and replacement are possible, by providing sufficient access and working room for testing and replacement.

Plumbing   At 'Second Fix' stage, the plumber's main tasks are to complete the installation of the central heating and to fix the sanitary fittings, WCs, basins, baths, showers, taps, etc. As with the electrician, the plumber is dependent upon the accuracy of his own work at 'First Fix' stage. In addition, he needs the attendance of the joiners, who must fix any additional bearers, battens, cradles and supports. Most of the exterior work to the building was completed at 'First Fix' stage, to ensure the building was made weathertight as soon as possible, but detail work remains to be done. Unlike the electrician, the plumber may physically not be able to complete an installation where there is not enough room to accommodate a fitting, for example between return walls, or where he does not have enough working space: this is a concern both of the preceding trades, who may have worked to the wrong tolerances, and of the designer, who may not have appreciated the problems he was causing. As with wiring, the routes of all piping should be carefully planned, especially where surface mounted, to ensure fixing is possible and that holes, ducts and chases are formed where required *(6.42)*. Finally, accesses for future maintenance must be carefully considered, especially for boilers, sanitary fittings, radiators, valves and cylinders.

Summary of plumbing 'Second Fix' points:
Check accuracy of positions of all pipe tails, waste connections, cisterns, cylinders, fixing brackets, bearers and battens
Ensure fittings will fit in the spaces provided
Management to ensure attendance as required from other trades, especially joiners
Ensure fittings are correctly fixed in the right locations in each space; for example, wall-mounted boilers in kitchens to be fixed accurately in relation to fuel and power feeds, flues and high level storage units
Ensure correct fittings are used
Check requirements of other trades, for example, in the installation of fire protection equipment
Programme work to ensure minimum interference with other trades
Designer to ensure routes for all surface-mounted pipework are properly planned and that fixing of pipes and fittings is possible; allow for expansion and contraction of concealed pipework
Designer to ensure sufficiently durable fittings are chosen in relation to agreed quality levels, cost and skills of the tradesmen
Installation to be fully tested upon completion; ensure both water and power supplies are available for this purpose
Ensure future replacement and maintenance are possible; provide access for de-mounting and fixing

Other trades   Apart from these principal trades, in many buildings a number of specialist finishing trades will be working. These include lift engineers, ventilation and air conditioning plant installers, cabinet makers, artists, specialist glaziers, suspended ceiling installers, floor layers, acoustic engineers, etc. Each trade will work both to its own accepted standards and to the quality levels agreed for the building, controlled by time and cost. Management must ensure that the work is correctly programmed, that any necessary attendance is provided, that continuity of working is possible, and that trades interfere as little as possible with each other. The designer can assist management by understanding what is required to carry out the piece of work he has designed and by trying to avoid a concentration of activity in a particular part of the building during critical stages of the finishing process, for example, by distributing services installations more evenly through the building shell.

(xix) Decoration   One of the final stages in the finishing and fitting of the building is the decoration of the exterior and interior. Quality as perceived by the client begins at this point during the handover of the building; the quality, or the lack of it, in the sub-strates and underlying structure will only become apparent during the succeeding months and years. Decoration includes paints, stains, varnishes and papers, including all preparatory work, but excludes the finishing work referred to in the preceding section.[82-89].

Externally, paints or stains are applied to woodwork and metals, although some metals and plastics are supplied pre-finished. It is also usual for woodwork to be supplied primed or pre-decorated, as in the case of stains. Internally, ceilings may be self-finished, as when tiled or suspended, or be painted or papered. Walls may be painted or papered, or, in the case of timber panelling, self-finished or varnished. Doors, windows and other trims are normally painted or self-finished.

Good preparation is essential for good finish: any marks on plaster surfaces or splits or shakes in timber will be apparent once paint is applied. On the other hand, paint, since it is an opaque coating, at least conceals surface marks, which stains do not. All timber surfaces must be carefully rubbed down, where not primed, and stopped and filled where necessary; knotting may be necessary on resinous surfaces unless a combined knotting and primer is used. Metal surfaces may require de-rusting prior to painting, either chemically or by sand-blasting. The integrity of anodised and plastics-coated surfaces must be checked both before and after assembly and any making good carried out.

The designer can do much to assist ease of decoration and subsequent maintenance by reducing painted and stained surfaces to a minimum, by considering the use of micro-porous paints, by designing components so that paints can be applied easily and will subsequently adhere, and by ensuring that access for maintenance is possible. He should also be aware that complex design may result in maintenance not being carried out, with resultant degrading (6.50).

Decoration may be carried out either by a firm's own men, or by sub-contractors. As with other trades, standards of finish must be agreed at the outset of the job and appropriate cost allowances made. Materials must be the best that can be afforded, be properly prepared and mixed, and be correctly applied. Storage under cover in a ventilated space is important. In

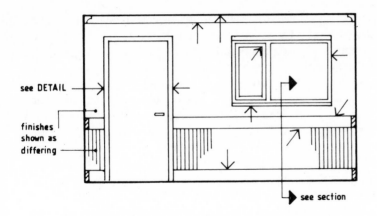

see DETAIL

finishes
shown as
differing

see section

ELEVATION of typical room   arrows indicate where special care needed

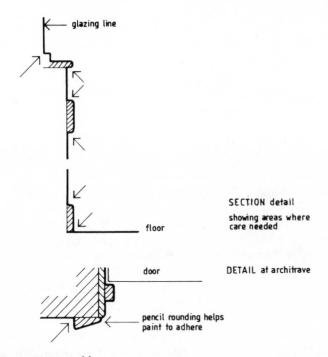

glazing line

SECTION detail

showing areas where
care needed

floor

door

DETAIL at architrave

pencil rounding helps
paint to adhere

6.50   *Decoration: problem areas*

exterior work, the stage at which painting is carried out will be dictated by the
stage at which the scaffolding is struck, unless the unsafe practice of working
off ladders is adopted. With interior work especially, agreement about the
final surface finish must be agreed with the joiners and other finishing trades.
The building must then be cleaned out and left dust-free before decoration
begins.

Quality points on decoration:
Designer to reduce *in situ* decorated surfaces to a minimum; design all

127

surfaces to be accessible for decoration; ensure paints will adhere to surfaces, for example, by pencil-rounding joinery arrises

Paints, stains, varnishes and papers to be stored correctly under cover in dry but ventilated spaces

Materials to be handled properly

Prepare all surfaces thoroughly: rub down and use where appropriate stopping, knotting, priming and de-rusting compounds; touch up self-finished surfaces where damaged

Apply paints, stains and varnishes as specified, in the correct number of coats; rub down if necessary between coats

Management to ensure adequate supervision of labour

Buildings to be accessible for decoration and to be dust and dirt-free: this will require co-ordination with other trades, especially joiners, plasterers, (for patching and screeding), electricians and other services specialists and scaffolders

Return visits may be necessary for touching in, but should be reduced to a minimum

Ensure surfaces can be maintained, whether by simple washing down or by re-painting or coating; avoid ledges, water traps and inaccessible areas, especially where acidic deposits are possible.

References

[81]Institute of Electrical Engineers, *Regulations for the electrical equipment of buildings*, IEE, 1974

[82]BRE, *Painting Walls* : Pts. 1 and 2, Digests 197, 198?, HMSO

[83]TRADA, *Finishes for outdoor timbers*, Wood Information Sheets 2/3–1, TRADA

[84]DoE, *Painting woodwork*, DoE Adivsory leaflet No. 25, HMSO

(xx) Floor and wall finishes: screeding and tiling

Screeding[85,86] will be necessary in many buildings where there is a solid concrete ground floor slab or where precast units or in situ slabs have been used at intermediate levels. The process takes place late in the building sequence so as to minimise damage to the screed prior to the laying of the floor finish. This inhibits access to parts of the building by other finishing trades and introduces 'wet' work at a stage when the building should be drying out. There may also be an adverse effect upon 'Second Fix' joinery items such as skirtings, which will absorb moisture from the screed, making them liable to movement and to fungal attack *(6.44)*. It is desirable, therefore, to leave the fixing of skirtings until after screeding, although this requires a return visit from the joiners. This applies particularly to floor-standing items such as kitchen units, which can only be installed once the building has dried out. The alternative to screeding is power-floating or early grinding, carried out shortly after the slab has been laid: this obviates screeding, but increases the risk of damage during later stages of building. This in turn may require the application of a surface filler before the laying of the floor finish. Another possibility to be considered by the designer is to avoid the use of thin surface finishes, such as vinyl tiles, which require a perfect sub-floor. A sub-floor deck, such as chipboard sheeting or t and g boarding, can be applied dry late in the job, avoiding the introduction of wet finishes and allowing the concrete slab to be left roughly tamped during the earlier stages of building. This is likely to incur a cost penalty, however. Skirtings can be made from some material other than timber, for example moulded plastic, which can be made to double as cover mouldings for electrical wiring or pipework.

Wall tiling Still widely used for protective and decorative purposes, especially in domestic interiors. Tiles are fragile and are often required to fit awkwardly shaped surfaces, for example round bathroom fittings; to window sills and reveals, and round duct covers. It is usual, especially in kitchens, to incorporate socket outlets in tiled surfaces, which requires tiles to be cut and the outlets to be fixed perfectly square in the wall. Designers should, therefore, wherever possible, design surfaces in terms of tile modules, both vertically and horizontally, which means taking account of room heights, positions of ducts, windows and doors, and the heights of floor and wall-mounted units and fittings. Socket outlets should, wherever possible, be located elsewhere than in a tiled surface, timber or moulded rail or surround *(6.51)*.

Floor tiling Requires perfect and dry surfaces, since every irregularity in the sub-floor will be apparent. If possible, room dimensions on plan between skirtings should be multiples of tile modules, allowing a small overlap beneath skirtings to take up slight variations in tile cutting and laying. Thicker tiles are less sensitive to poor sub-floors than thin ones.

Quality points on screeding and tiling:
Screeding
Consider whether screeding is necessary: for example, can power floating or
  early grinding be substituted? Can alternative materials or a thicker tiled
  finish be laid? Is asphalting an acceptable alternative?
Ensure tamped floors are scabbled prior to screeding
Ensure floors are protected during the construction process if early grinding
  or power-floating are used
Programme the work to ensure minimal disruption to the other trades
  working in the building
Fix skirtings after screeding or use materials other than timber; consider using
  de-mountable skirtings to conceal services
Ensure screeding materials are correctly stored, handled and mixed before
  application; allow for protection and curing after laying
Management to co-ordinate work carefully, especially if this is a sub-contract
  item.

Wall tiling
Consider wall tiling modules; designers to design in tile modules whenever
  possible
Avoid awkward junctions, returns and angles, for example at windows, ducts,
  round fittings and adjacent to units

129

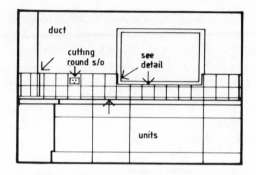

tiling the kitchen : arrows indicate problem areas

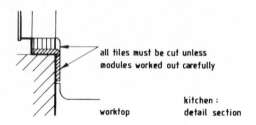

all tiles must be cut unless
modules worked out carefully

kitchen :

worktop   detail section

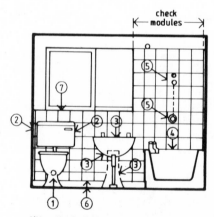

tiling the bathroom : problem areas

① at pan outlet

② round cistern

③ round cantilevered basin; behind pedestal

④ round top of bath

⑤ at fittings such as showers

⑥ at skirtings

⑦ at cills

6.51 *Wall tiling: difficult areas*

130

Locate socket outlets, cooker points, etc, elsewhere than in tiled surfaces

Tiles to be firmly bedded on smooth, firm (inflexible) backings, with joints neatly pointed

Consider using laminated and other sheet materials, such as plastics-faced timber sheet instead of tiles, especially where subsequent access behind surfaces is needed

Avoid use of odd-shaped and patterned tiles, which will be difficult to replace in later years.

Floor tiling

If thin vinyl, ensure sub-finish is perfect, if necessary by using filling compound or by screeding just prior to tiling

Ensure screed has fully dried

Consider use of less sensitive finishes, such as pvc, linoleum, or patterned materials to disguise irregularities

Design rooms to floor tiling modules where possible, noting that tolerances can be critical

Tiles to be correctly prepared for laying; use correct adhesive or bedding compound; set out accurately

Management to co-ordinate work carefully, especially if this is a sub-contract item.

Other factors

Where floors are liable to attack from corrosive substances, special materials will be needed for both sub-floor and finishes; ensure, therefore, that the likely uses of the building are known before designing the floors.

References

[85]Barnbrook, G, *Laying floor screeds*, C & CA
[86]BRE, *Floor screeds*, Digest 104, HMSO

(xxi) External works: landscaping Apart from cleaning up, 'snagging' and commissioning, decoration completes the interior of the buildings. Whilst the final stages of building work proceed, and after striking the scaffolding, work to the surrounding areas can take place. It is important to ensure that clean access to the building is maintained for the interior tradesmen, especially in bad weather, to prevent dirt being carried inside. The most likely source of trouble is late completion of the underground services by the Statutory Boards, since service trenches run close to the buildings and are usually dug separately and at different times by each Board *(6.05)*. Apart from the difficulty and danger of carrying fragile and sensitive materials across lines of trenching, there is the need to lay on services as soon as possible after 'First Fix' is complete, to enable systems to be tested. If this is not possible, temporary fuel and water supplies must be provided, incurring extra cost and another problem for management. This is also the stage for final testing and flushing out of drains, including the completion of manholes and rodding eyes, and the final setting of gulleys and channels.

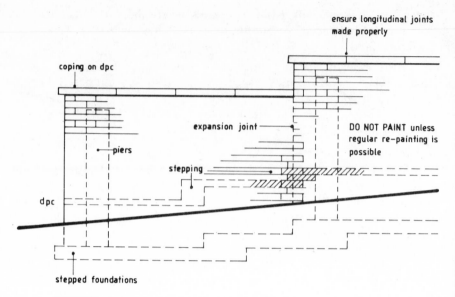

coping on dpc

ensure longitudinal joints
made properly

expansion joint

DO NOT PAINT unless
regular re-painting is
possible

piers

stepping

dpc

stepped foundations

ELEVATION : typical stepped screen wall

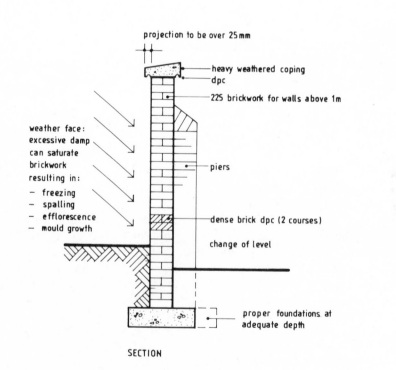

projection to be over 25mm

heavy weathered coping
dpc

225 brickwork for walls above 1m

weather face:
excessive damp
can saturate
brickwork
resulting in:

– freezing
– spalling
– efflorescence
– mould growth

piers

dense brick dpc (2 courses)

change of level

proper foundations at
adequate depth

SECTION

6.52   *Screen walls: problem areas*

If roads were designed to run close to buildings and were completed to base course level, reasonably good access to buildings will have been provided during the course of construction. Once surfaces have been cleaned, the wearing course can be laid by the roadworks contractor, care being taken to lay to proper camber and falls. Once this work is complete, rainwater run-off will start and gulleys and sewers must be tested and in good working condition. Work to hard-standings and paths can also be carried out and, again, gulleys and drains must be fully operational.

Electrical work includes the erection of lamp standards and the connection of any lighting to public areas in and around the building.

Screen walls and fences may be required (6.52)[87,88]. Bricklayers should not have to return to the job to build screen walls, which should therefore be phased to follow an earlier stage of bricklaying on the building. Quality of work is important, since screen walls are easily seen and can dramatically affect the appearance of the completed job. Particular attention should be paid to dpcs, to stability, which can be affected by the type of dpc, to countering the risk of undue wetting of weather faces, leading to effloresc-ence and frost attack, and to coping details; copings must be designed to ensure that water is shed clear of the wall face and be heavy enough to stay in position.

Fences, if of timber, should be weathered to shed water, be supported on posts, stoned and tamped rather than concreted into place to make replacement easier, and be constructed of suitably treated timbers (6.53). Painted fences are expensive and tedious to maintain, especially if parts are difficult to reach, and may degrade rapidly. The erection of fences and of less durable screens should proceed in step with the reinstatement of topsoil and with the planting of trees and shrubs.

Landscaping[89] Both hard and soft may be specified. Hard landscaping includes pavings to terraces and paths, decorated walling and a variety of other features. Soft landscaping includes earth formation and mounding, consolidating where necessary, the planting of trees and shrubs and the provision of new sub-soil drainage. This work is almost invariably sub-contracted, including design where proposals are complex. Earth may have to be brought on site, unless enough has been stockpiled at the begining of the job (6.01). Carting distances should be as short as possible, and for this reason the landscaping proposals should be available by the date of contract start, at the latest. Plant for handling trees and for earth-moving may sometimes be large. This can damage roads, kerbs, manholes and existing planting unless great care is taken.

Quality factors in external works include:
Ensure clean accesses are maintained for interior trades carrying in easily damaged materials and components
Ensure work by the Statutory Boards is completed as early as possible, to reduce the amount of trenching and to enable testing of internal services to be carried out

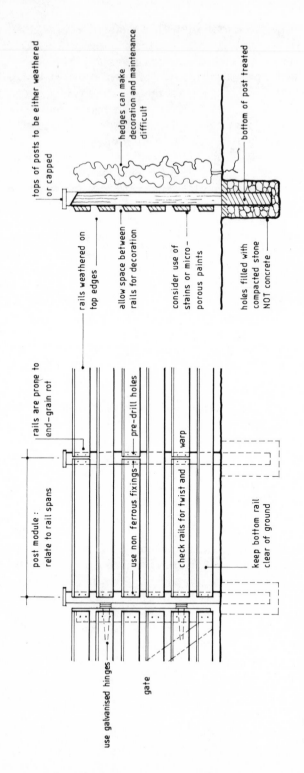

tops of posts to be either weathered or capped

hedges can make decoration and maintenance difficult

bottom of post treated

rails weathered on top edges

allow space between rails for decoration

consider use of stains or micro-porous paints

holes filled with compacted stone NOT concrete

section

rails are prone to end-grain rot

post module : relate to rail spans

pre-drill holes

use non ferrous fixings

warp

check rails for twist and

keep bottom rail clear of ground

use galvanised hinges

gate

elevation typical fence and gate

6.53   *Post and rail fences: problem areas*

Flush out and test completed drainage installations

Finish laying roads, paths and hardstandings; test gulleys, drains and sewers

Install electrical items: lamp standards, public lighting, etc, and test

Build screen walls and fences: ensure that walls are stable and resistant to weather; ensure that fences are stable, weather resistant and easy to maintain

Reinstate sub- and top-soil, relating this work to fencing, to sub-soil drainage and to any specialist landscape work

Plant trees and shrubs; avoid planting large trees too close to buildings

Ensure all materials are properly stored, handled and brought on site according to programme

Design of all landscaping to be complete by date of contract to enable planting to proceed without delay

Use plant carefully to avoid damaging other external works.

References
[87]National Building Agency, *External works detail sheets*, NBA, 1977
[88]Korff, *Design of freestanding walls*, BDA, 1983
[89]Weddle, A E, *Landscape techniques*, Heinemann, 1979

(xxii) Job completion and maintenance   Once landscaping is complete, apart from the final planting and securing of trees and shrubs which may take place over a number of months during the growing season, and once the building has been handed over, the job is finished and the maintenance period begins. This extends for between six and twelve months, depending upon which parts of the building are involved: heating and air conditioning plants, for example, will have to go through a complete annual heating and cooling cycle before being accepted by many building owners.

Assuming that no major structural weakness becomes apparent, work during the maintenance period includes the correcting of surface defects and those which can appear as the building settles gradually under its own weight and acquires its permanent levels of moisture content and chemical stability. Designers have a major responsibility to ensure that this adjustment can take place with minimal failures in detailing and materials, for example, by not specifying brittle plasters on top of unreinforced junctions in sub-strates and by ensuring that joinery components overlap each other, so that movement can be accommodated without cracks appearing.

With many buildings, perhaps the majority, there will not have been enough time to allow for full drying out of wet work. Thus re-decoration of originally damp surfaces or of areas where cracks and faults have appeared may be necessary. Designers can help to reduce the risk of this by working in dry construction as much as possible, or by ensuring at least that any trapped moisture can escape. Components should be installed to adequate tolerances and be free to move in relation to each other.

Quality points on job completion and maintenance
Agree maintenance periods for the different elements of the building *(6.54)*.

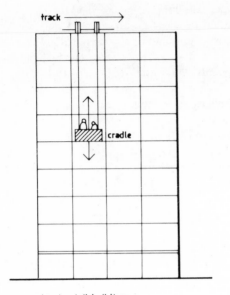

cleaning tall buildings

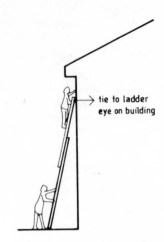

maintenance from ladders can be dangerous

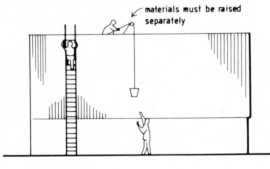

ladder access to roofs

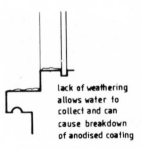

extruded alloy cills

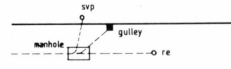

cleaning drains and wastes

cleaning valleys and gutters : access should be provided

6.54 *Maintenance: Typical problem areas*

Establish an inspection programme for the maintenance period

Check for movement in materials and adjoining components both visually and where necessary check by using suitable measuring devices

Design for movement: for example, avoid using brittle materials where movement is likely; use an 'overlap joint' technique when designing joinery components; allow for movement in large surfaces and in materials with a high coefficient of thermal expansion; provide expansion joints, gaskets and seals

Allow for the possible cost and inconvenience of early re-decoration

Use 'dry' construction wherever possible, to control the chemical and physical effects of drying out.

7   Quality and cost

(a) Initial cost

It was stated in Chapter 1 that quality could be defined in terms of purpose, technical performance, appearance and experience, controlled by the overriding parameters of cost and time. It is now necessary to consider the effects of these parameters upon building cost[1]. To do this we must consider, first, the initial building cost, together with the time taken to design and build and secondly, the cost of the building over its lifespan. It will then be possible to review the effect of time upon these processes.

The initial building cost contains all those cost elements which arise from the time the building is conceived to the day on which it is handed over as a functioning entity. They include:

(i)   management time in developing the brief
(ii)   appointment and briefing of consultants
(iii)   preparation of initial design proposals
(iv)   costing studies
(v)   obtaining approvals
(vi)   detail design documentation
(vii)   appointing the builder (tender and contract)
(viii) building the building
(ix)   commissioning and handing over.

Various methods are available for procuring buildings, varying from lump sum and cost plus contracts, through management fee to full 'design and build'. Each has cost implications and the choice of method can markedly affect quality. Broadly, however, the cost-sensitive areas within each of the stages referred to above are the same for most types of building procurement.

(i) Developing the brief

This may involve initially only one person, or a small team set up within the client organisation to define the requirements for the new building. Decisions at this stage may crucially affect quality on site, however, for example by deciding to go for a 'fast-track', 'high-tech' solution rather than one more conservatively conceived. Unless the following decisions are consistent with these early ones, there may be a poor fit between performance and cost: the wrong designer may be chosen, followed by the wrong builder. Cost penalties will then be incurred through having to 'educate' various members of the team and from having to correct errors. Given this risk, one of the most cost-effective decisions which the client might make initially would be to appoint a client representative or project manager, either from inside or outside the organisation, to control the project from inception to completion:

138

this person's function would be to ensure that the building was built to time, to the right cost limits and at the agreed quality levels.

(ii) Appointing and briefing consultants[2]

This can be a frustrating and expensive experience for both client and consultant if they do not agree about objectives, if a consultant is inexperienced in the kind of work envisaged or if the basis for remuneration of the consultant is unsatisfactory. Since consultants' fees can amount to some 12–15% of project building costs, the choice of consultants can be critical: not only will fees have to be allowed for within the budget, but if the wrong decisions are taken by the consultants, building costs themselves will be increased. On the other hand, a good team of consultants can make savings on building cost whilst maintaining or enhancing quality.

A fundamental decision to be taken at this stage is whether a separate design team is required. It may be desirable to appoint a 'design and build' organisation to carry out the work, especially where time is short. However, in this case, a different approach to quality would be required. For example, a client might be well advised to protect quality by appointing an 'in-house' or independent consultant to advise him on the performance of the design-builders, but it would be essential to ensure that this person's remit was limited to advice and did not include direct dealing with the design and building teams.

In summary, the main factors to be taken into account when making appointments are:

experience possessed by the consultants in the type of work proposed
scope of each consultant's work; this will affect the size of team
fees required; likely level of expenses.

(iii) Initial design proposals

These will establish the main outlines of the project and show possible alternative ways in which the brief can be satisfied. They will inevitably carry with them the seeds of future conflict, unless they respect the constraints on cost and time which the client has imposed. For example, a building system may be proposed which can be erected quickly to known standards of quality and at a predictable cost; it may be accompanied, however, by a complex set of external and internal claddings and finishes which will delay the programme and distort the cost predictions. This may be acceptable for a prestige or one-off building, but for most clients an area of uncertainty will have been created. For this reason amongst others, cost estimates must accompany initial design proposals, together with assessments of quality type and level required, making realistic, that is probably pessimistic, assumptions about the performance likely to be achieved.

(iv) Cost studies

These have already been referred to in relation to the preparation of initial design proposals. They must be prepared at all stages of the design process, however, and the client kept fully informed. In terms of quality, the objective is to obtain 'value for money': this is much easier to do where the availability and performance of materials, components and sub-assemblies is well known. The difficulty arises when unfamiliar components are chosen and where the interfaces or junctions between components and sub-assemblies have not been tested. The job should be broken down, therefore, into categories, varying from the totally predictable to the totally unknown. Bricklaying ordinary quality facings in a normal exposure setting might be an example of the former, and suspending a roof from posts and steel cables an instance of the latter. Where repetition is likely, test panels or assemblies can be made, preferably full size, to 'de-bug' any problems, bearing in mind the cost of doing this. Unless a great deal of money is available, to do a 'dry run' on a one-off building or sub-assembly may not be justified, whereas it may be fully justified when developing, say, a new house type with a complex set of interfaces round the kitchen and service areas. The use of models, or of manufacturers' own facilities, can reduce the costs of testing, albeit at the risk of their not being fully realistic or objective, thereby reducing the value of this approach. Broadly, the philosophy of design should vary from conservatism, that is design with a high predictability factor, where performance to known levels of quality has to be guaranteed, to innovation, justified only where the high risks involved are acceptable to the client.

(v) Obtaining approvals This is an essential part of the design process and as such cannot be avoided. Substantial delays can be incurred, however, with consequent cost implications, if a design is unfamiliar to planners and building control officers. Inability to satisfy planners may result in a public enquiry, which can be extremely expensive and time-consuming, and a client should consider this possibility if he commissions a highly unusual building on a sensitive urban site or on one with great landscape value. On the other hand, technical innovation may incur the cost of tests to prove performance, where building components and assemblies are not covered by 'deemed-to-satisfy' clauses or where standards differing from those in the Regulations are proposed. Again, this can be time-consuming and expensive. The answer is for designers to possess complete familiarity with all relevant planning and Regulation requirements, including any special regulations which may affect the building proposed, for example those to do with fire or industrial safety. Where time-saving is important, either the design must be as acceptable as possible to the Authorities in order to minimise the risk of rejection, or consultation with official bodies must begin as soon as the initial design proposals are agreed with the client. In fact, discussions with planners may well be desirable during the feasibility stage, to establish whether or not a building or any sort is likely to get approval.

(vi) Detail design
During this stage, final design decisions will be taken and quality standards established by the use of written descriptions and references. All the points made already with reference to cost and quality apply, but with even more force. For instance, it will become fully apparent at this stage where assembly

complications are likely to occur, which materials and components will be hard to obtain and which parts of the work are so specialised that they will have to be sub-contracted, thereby incurring uncertainty in the area of management control and costing. The penalties for taking wrong decisions become greater now also, since the design will have become integrated – it will be impossible to change one part without changing all the rest (7.01) – and since there will be an increasing time constraint to proceed. It is at this stage, therefore, that the benefits of having the builder involved in the design process can become significant, since he will be able to bring his practical knowledge to bear and help to reduce uncertainties. This will in turn make cost prediction easier, enabling the client to maintain his financial control of the project. At this stage, also, areas of financial uncertainty must be reduced to a minimum. For example, provisional sums should be avoided if possible since, if these are intended to cover undesigned parts of the building, it will be impossible to advise the client with certainty what the final cost of the building will be.

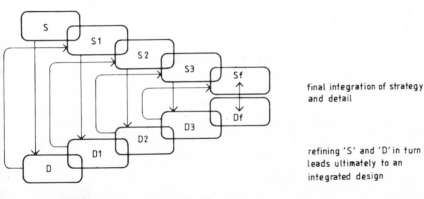

final integration of strategy and detail

refining 'S' and 'D' in turn leads ultimately to an integrated design

7.01 *Interlocking of strategy and detail*

(vii) Appointing the builder The need to appoint a builder capable of building at the agreed quality levels has already been discussed (chapter 3). This is important also from the point of view of cost: a builder may be able to offer a fast and efficient service on the larger contract, but may perform inefficiently on the smaller one, since his overheads will be high in relation to the value of the job. Theoretically, such a builder would be excluded automatically during competitive tendering, unless there were other reasons why he wanted the work forcing him to distort his price, but where a contract was negotiated and the price agreed did not reflect the builder's costs accurately the risk of appointing the wrong builder might be a real one. A more likely situation occurs when a smaller builder tenders for a job beyond his competence: in this case, the demand for a certain level of performance may first of all confuse him, then result in claims, as he tries to recover the costs of his incompetence. By appointing the builder early in the design process, it is possible not only to agree achieveable quality levels in relation to

141

cost and competence in building, but also to allow the builder the necessary time to adjust his organisation to the requirements of the building process, for example, by assessing his needs for certain types of labour and plant and by arranging the optimum distribution of labour between himself and his sub-contractors. Once the builder has been selected, the choice of contract must give both client and builder the opportunity to strike a reasonable bargain for the building. This must include guarantees about competence from the builder and about the provision of information and regular payment from the client. The other crucial element is the need to allow for some means of settling disputes, including claims and arbitration. Broadly, before work begins on site, it must have been clearly agreed by all parties what is to be built, to what standard, over what period of time and at what cost. Failure in any of these elements is bound to result in delay, higher costs and poorer quality once work begins.

(viii) Building process Once the design has been completed, the documentation produced and the contract made, the builder should be able to move on site and build to the agreed quality levels and costs. The reasons why he might not be able to do so include incomplete information, unexpected delays in the course of the works due, for example, to poor ground conditions and bad weather, and changes in the design. The cost implications of delays and changes once work has begun can be quite significant and can lead to claims and arbitration. For example, extra costs can be incurred as a result of unforeseen difficulty in completing work below ground: this gives the builder the choice of either absorbing the costs and of trying to recover them later in the job by taking short cuts, or of agreeing a reasonable extra on the basis of remeasurement. One way round such a problem might be to have a contract which is a composite between 'lump sum' for work above ground (including superstructure, finishes and fittings) and 'cost plus' for work below ground, although a reasonable maximum limit to this would have to be set. Many problems with substructures can, of course, be obviated by thorough site investigation, especially where 'made' ground is suspected or where there has been mining or subsidence, and money must be allowed for this and for archive research during the early design stages. Poor weather can affect quality of build and increase costs by causing delays and by making it difficult to carry out work. Again, substructures are likely to be the worst affected area owing, for example, to waterlogging of trenches. Also, mud on site can make site transit handling difficult and low temperatures can prevent concreting and bricklaying. Designers and project planners can do much to minimise the effects of bad weather: trench fill concreting reduces the amount of substructure brickwork, roads can be laid during fine weather and early in the job to allow access for plant and deliveries and concrete finishing can be carried out under cover. It may also be possible to programme the work so that superstructures are completed during better weather, leaving finishes and fittings until the winter months.

Accurate documentation and the reasons for minimising changes in design and quality standards have already been discussed (chapter 4). It must be emphasised, however, that inadequate drawings, instructions and references can both delay the works and provide an excellent basis for claims, thereby increasing the cost of the job. Cost effects can, indeed, become open-ended when changes are made, since, owing to the integrating of all elements in a design, a change in one part can cause repercussions throughout the building, with unforeseeable financial consequences *(7.01)*. For this reason, amongst others, regular cost reports to the client as work proceeds are essential.

(iv) Handing over   Once the building is built, it must be cleaned, commissioned and handed over. Money must be allowed for this process, which in a highly serviced building can be a lengthy and critical operation. For example, lifts must be adjusted, water services and sprinkler systems tested and communications systems checked. Tradesmen may have to attend on the specialists during this work since, where defects are elusive, dismantling and reconstruction may be necessary.

(b) Life cycle costs

After completion and handing over, the life of the building begins. At the initial stage, during inception and the development of the brief, the client must consider what his financial commitment to the building will be once it is in use. Having occupied the new building, returns will begin from mortgage, renting or leasing, but money will have to be set aside for maintenance, replacement and for any anticipated depreciation on the building and its site. A critical factor in replacement costs will be the durability both of the parts of the building and of the building as a whole, and the anticipated life of the components and sub-assemblies should be assessed. This will affect the design and building stages in two principal ways: in the quality of components used and in the level of skill needed to fix them. The designer, meanwhile, can assist durability and maintenance by 'designing in' easy access to and desmountability of concealed parts of the building, especially services, and by specifying agreed quality levels not only for the components themselves but also for their maintenance and replacement.

The client, in assessing his commitment to the building, must consider at feasibility stage the trade-off between initial and life cycle costs. For example, is the building to be a low first cost, high life cycle cost building, as with a new form of system-built housing, or are both to be high, as with a prestige, one-off commercial building? This decision affects the initial design approach, as has already been stressed, and it must therefore be made both before and during the briefing of consultants. One way of conducting the exercise would be to construct high and low risk profiles giving the best and worst implications of certain decisions and trade-offs *(7.02)*. For example, is image more important than long building life or do the financial constraints impose a long building life, with low maintenance costs, implying conservative design in long-lasting and well-tried materials and components? Such questions must be raised and answered before the quality levels can be agreed, the design carried out and the building built.

Once the building is in occupation, a reassessment of quality levels can be made. This should attempt to measure achieved standards against those originally proposed, possibly by using the diagrams suggested earlier (2.01(a),(b)). For example, if achieved quality levels fell within the 'triangle' defined by client's, designer's and builder's standards, measured using one of the methods described in Appendix 1, success could be claimed. The final stage in the exercise would be to project new quality standards for the building over its anticipated life, enabling realistic cost estimates for maintenance and replacement to be made.

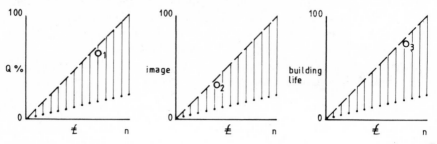

7.02   *High and low risk profiles*

References

[1]Davis, Belfield and Everest (ed), *Spon's Architects' and Builders' Price Book* : 1985 edition, Spon

[2]*Architect's appointment : main and small works*, RIBA Publications 1982

8 Quality and time

(a) Time to completion

The second major parameter affecting quality on site through its influence upon purpose, technical performance, appearance and experience, is that of time. As was noted in the Introduction, the client's decisions about time available to design and build will affect not only the size and complexity of the project but also the choice of builder, the method of contracting and the way in which the building is constructed. Furthermore, where life cycle costs must be minimised, a durable, well-detailed building is needed, achieving which may be a relatively slow process. On the other hand, the client may be prepared to run the risk of high life-cycle costs in return for a rapidly completed building, using advanced technology whose durability cannot be guaranteed, accepting that maintenance costs may be high.

At the *feasibility* stage, when the client is developing the brief, certain important decisions about time must be taken. For example, how soon is the building required (this must be a realistic calculation, since every building is needed 'as soon as possible')? How much time is available for researching and developing new building techniques and components? What resources are available for managing, designing and building the project? How durable need the building be? Decisions must be supported by calculations covering estimates of cost versus returns on the project, suggesting, for example, fast or slow-track programmes or delays between phases, perhaps in order to match rate of build to anticipated rate of sale or leasing.

Building size and complexity   A very large building will generally take longer to build than a small one, unless the large one is built using rapid-building techniques and the small one by traditional methods. The major problem is the degree of 'uniqueness' required in the building. Clients may be open-minded about this, but some designers design even a well-understood building type, such as a school, as though it had never been done before. In fact, the only convincing reasons for uniqueness in an established building type are the site, which will be different for every new building, and changes in fashion, where time plays a part. Indeed, for many corporate clients, fashion, or the presentation of an up-to-date corporate image, may be important. Given comparable building methods, however, the large and complex building will take longer to build, simply because more materials and components have to be assembled on site and fitted together. Time to complete the process can be reduced, however, by using as many standard materials, components and sub-assemblies as possible and by reducing the variety of joints and junctions to a minimum. To do this will improve both the quality of the completed building and its durability, since uncertainty has been reduced and since supervisors and operatives will have less to learn about each new operation.

Specifically, time to completion can be reduced, and predicted levels of quality made more certain by:
- reducing size to a minimum
- planning the building as simply as possible
- where large size is unavoidable, repeating planning modules (as with bays in a factory, or floors in a multi-storey building)
- where complexity is unavoidable, combining smaller standardised elements in various ways to form the necessary unique larger elements *(8.01)*
- using proven and tested materials, components and jointing techniques
- reducing the number and variety of joints and junctions;
- commissioning research and development well ahead in the pre-contract programme
- accepting realistic probability of success when using new materials and building techniques; in other words, budgeting for a percentage of failure
- careful selection, briefing and training of design and building teams
- selection of the appropriate contract method
- clear financial planning
- clear and effective management decision-making, including realistic and tightly controlled programming
- considering carefully the trade-off between initial and life-cycle costs.

Choice of builder   It is worth repeating that, for all but the smallest jobs, time can usually be saved by selecting the builder early in the design process. This brings the builder into job planning at the stage when his advice about practical matters can be incorporated and can be most effective. Only for a very small number and type of jobs, perhaps those where the aesthetic aims of the client and the designer coincide, is there a case for leaving the appointment of builder until the design has been completed; even then, the design intention can be prejudiced and delays can occur if the builder does not understand clearly what is required or is unable to build to the required standard.

Builders should be chosen who are capable of building at the speed required by the client. To achieve completion on time, good management by all parties – client, designer and builder – is essential. The builder in particular must be capable of organising the production process, as described in chapter 5, and of deploying a site team with the appropriate skills. He may also have to manage a number of sub-contractors working under different constraints of time and cost, which means good programming before the job starts and tight control once it is running. This is very difficult with traditional contract methods and, where close control of time and budget is essential, clients are often best served by choosing one of the alternative methods of building procurement. The objective should be to simplify communication between designers and builders, enabling designers to take full account of the building process and builders to programme all pre-contract research, including design, in a co-ordinated way.

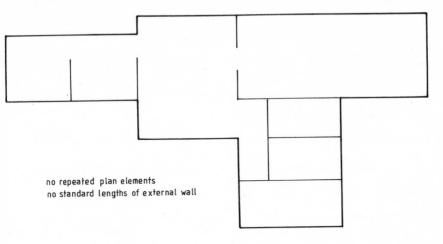

no repeated plan elements
no standard lengths of external wall

building plans can be rationalised to permit the maximum repetition of plan elements, whilst retaining overall variety

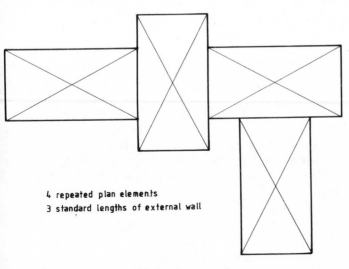

4 repeated plan elements
3 standard lengths of external wall

8.01   *Non-repeated and repeated plan elements*

Contract method   The need to select a contract method appropriate to the time available for building has already been referred to. To emphasise this point, where programmes are tight, solutions must be found quickly. Conversely, where a high-risk, highly innovative building is commissioned, the earliest possible involvement by the builder can yield dividends. On the other hand, traditional contracting methods may be suitable where time limits are fairly relaxed, where design is conservative and where funds are more freely available. It may even be worth considering using relatively open-ended methods, such as cost-plus, where both client and designer agree that factors other than cost and time should over-rule. The effects of various constraints upon the choice of contract method can be summarised as follows:

Constraints	Contract method
Time short	Negotiation
Simple design	Management fee
Innovative design	
Funds limited	Design/build
Plenty of time	
Conservative design	Lump sum
Funds freely available	
Aesthetic constraints over-rule	Cost plus

A combination of different methods may also be worth considering, especially where uncertainty, including that over time, must be reduced. The example of 'cost plus' for work below ground, combined with 'lump sum' for superstructures has already been cited. Also worth considering is one of several forms of two-stage tendering, useful when choice of the right builder is of paramount importance.

Method of building   This will have a major effect upon time and quality. The choice of building method is implicit in the design and designers must be aware of this. For example, by describing precisely what is to be done, and in what order, the designer may be defining an optimum building method for one particular builder, but even then only for one thoroughly familiar with the building process; other builders tendering for the work might find this building method expensive. On the other hand, by describing the design intention in outline only, perhaps by performance standards, different builders will be free to make their own decisions about building method, which will reflect their desire to make the job pay, but which may not be in the best interests of the client or the designer. This problem has been discussed in chapter 2 in terms of agreed quality levels and the need for compromise in fixing AQL 1 and 2 (see (2.01)).

Where time is short, the method of building must take account of this fact, following either a high or a low risk profile. An example of the former would be where corners were cut and a highly innovative 'system' design was developed to meet the target handover date, and of the latter where a greatly simplified and conservative design was used, where the building method was well known. Whichever approach is chosen, the risks should be properly assessed before either client or designer commit themselves and, once the builder is involved, he should be asked to prepare a method statement, describing how he intends to carry out the work. If such a statement were submitted with the tender, it would be possible to alter the design to take

148

ccount of the building process.

Typical interactions between methods of building and time for different forms of superstructure can be summarised as follows:

Method	Time to completion
Traditional, masonry; eg rationalised traditional low-rise, non-innovative design	Predictable, since method well known Relatively lengthy
Timber frame (ditto)	Predictable Much reduced, unless cladding and finishing complex
Standard steel frame (medium span, medium rise)	Predictable Frame erection fast, but fire-proofing may slow progress Completion depends on decking, roofing, cladding and finishing
In situ, reinforced concrete frame (medium span; medium/high rise)	Predictable Frame erection fast if rapid shuttering and/or special cement ratios chosen. Completion as for steel
Precast concrete frame (use as for 'in situ' frame)	Predictable Frame erection fast, provided jointing kept simple Completion as steel Note: Overall contract time should take account of need for off-site fabrication.
Composite and innovative methods	Unpredictable Research and development may be needed Completion as for steel.

(b) Quality during the building's life

The principle factor affecting quality during the building's life is durability. This applies to the whole building as a system and to the sub-systems from which it is made up. Since these sub-systems interact, failure in one may affect the performance of others and of the whole building. The client must decide first, in co-operation with the designer, whether the building is to be durable and if so over what period of time. For example, a cathedral might be expected to last for centuries, but a warehouse for ten years. The second order decision concerns whether the whole building is to be equally durable in all its parts, or whether some parts can be allowd to fail sooner than others. Finally, it must be agreed what level of maintenance is needed to secure the durability both of the whole building and of its sub-systems according to the pattern decided.

In summary:

    Decision level 1: How durable should the building be as a complete system?

    Decision level 2: What are the acceptable lives of the sub-systems?

    Decision level 3: What level of maintenance input is needed to secure performances agreed in 1 and 2?

The durability of the building depends upon the care taken in both design and construction, and includes such factors as whether the design is conservative or innovative, the thoroughness of research and development, the accuracy in specification of materials and components, the design of joints and junctions, the selection of builder, the quality of supervision and the performance by the operatives. These factors have already been discussed separately in previous chapters. Regardless of how well the building is built, however, and however good the maintenance, components and system will fail and will have to be replaced. It may be possible to predict the likely order or sequence of failure and to plan for preventive maintenance. An example would be the batch replacement of fluorescent tubes. Since cost can be high, however, every effort must be made to establish the likely frequency of maintenance and replacement and to ensure the work can be done easily. For example, where short-life items have to be replaced or lubrication of mechanisms has to be carried out, components should be accessible and easy to dismantle. Also, the labour skill levels should be consistent with these factors, the most frequently serviced items having a lower labour skill content than the least frequently serviced ones.

The principal factor in making maintenance easy is ensuring ease of inspection: this includes both visual inspection and testing. Failure of a light bulb is immediately obvious and replacement usually straightforward, though not always so with some complex and concealed fittings. Corrosion of a steel frame, on the other hand, as with some post-war, system-build housing, may not be apparent until gross failure has occurred. Designers should allow, therefore, for the simplest possible replacement of short-life items and regular inspection of all building components, either by ensuring access so that visual inspection is possible or by the use of monitoring and testing facilities, for example by the provision of hygrometers to measure condensation levels in external walls. As already mentioned, the skill levels needed to carry out regular replacement and inspection should be matched to both the frequency and the difficulty of doing the work.

With conservatively designed buildings, where the building techniques are well known and materials, components and jointing systems have predictable performance, good durability and easy maintenance are likely: the materials of which the building has been built will probably continue to be available over long periods of time, as will operatives skilled in this kind of work. With innovative design, on the other hand, durability is likely to be prejudiced in several different ways: the assembly of the building, because unfamiliar to the operatives, may not have been done properly; there may have been insufficient research and development into new materials, components and assembly techniques; replacement of components and assemblies may be inherently difficult, and the components and the skills to fix them may no longer be available after the building has been in use for a few years; an example is the use of a complex hingeing system in 'high performance' windows. To settle for a highly innovative building, therefore, may be to invite a high risk of failure and of difficulty in replacing parts once failure does occur. The only ways to avoid this risk, or at least to minimise it, are first, to carry out regular inspections, secondly, to build in a relatively high level of 'redundnacy', so that components will not fail until severe degrading has taken place and, thirdly, to make the innovative parts from well-tried and tested components of simpler design, jointing them in straightforward ways.

In summary, 'quality' during a building's life can be improved by:
  - designing the building properly in the first place
  - carrying out all research and development thoroughly
  - building with care to agreed quality levels
  - deciding how long the building should last as a complete system
  - designing for 'failure precedence', allowing some systems to fail before others
  - fully briefing the client and building users on maintenance requirements
  - planning maintenance schedules to meet failure precedence profiles; carrying out preventive maintenance
  - designing for easy replacement of short-life items
  - designing for easy inspection and testing of all building components and sub-assemblies; ensuring replacement is straightforward
  - matching labour skill levels to the likely frequency of replacement of components
  - assessing the risk of failure in terms of building design, depending upon, for example, whether this is conservative or innovative
  - minimising maintenance cost in innovative buildings by variety reduction and through the maximum use of standard components and sub-assemblies, by building in relatively high levels of redundancy and by regular inspection.

151

9 Quality and modernisation

Modernisation, or refurbishment, of buildings is undertaken for many reasons[1].

For example:
- the upgrading of amenities and facilities to meet currently acceptable standards
- the replacement of obsolete or perished elements of the fabric of the building
- improvement or changes to the interior of the building
- the improvement of external amenities and facilities.

Quality in modernisation, as with new buildings, can be assessed in terms of purpose, functional performance, appearance and experience, all related to the parameters of cost and time. The brief should be developed in terms of these criteria, bearing in mind that the success of a modernisation project will depend initially upon the designer having a true appreciation of the client's requirements. To achieve this, he must make an accurate and detailed assessment of the condition of the building or buildings and of what will be required to satisfy the client.

The contractor appointed will also require detailed knowledge, in order to meet the client's requirements without damaging or disturbing those parts of the building which are to be retained. In some cases this may mean working around occupiers still in residence during the modernisation process.

Meticulous planning and programming of a modernisation project is vital if success is to be achieved, especially where 'decanting' has not taken place. For example, it should be recognised that the major alteration of one's home can be a traumatic experience for an occupier and that initial preparations will require tact, patience and understanding from client, designer and contractor. At the very least, tenants require to know when work will be carried out, what re-organisation of their normal routine will occur, what will happen to their furniture during the work, how quickly the property will be returned to an acceptable degree of comfort and what the finished job will be like.

Sometimes modernisation has to be carried out whilst retaining the existing appearances of the building, for example when preservation orders apply, but usually the work can be broken down into three stages:

(a) *Demolition or removal*
(b) *Installation of major new elements*
(c) *Fittings and finishes.*

(a) Demolition

Before demolition takes place, the building fabric and finishes must be carefully surveyed and measured to ensure that the likely full extent of the works is known and that an accurate cost base is established. Often, this is the first time that it will have been possible to gain free entry to the building and it is especially important at this stage to gain the full co-operation of the occupier. In addition to listing items for removal and the parts of the building which will have to be replaced, the possibility of re-use of items should be considered; where this is not possible, it may nevertheless be possible to sell off components and materials and credit the returns to the contract. Another important factor is the extent of concealed decay and degradation of the fabric, which may not be apparent until superimposed elements are removed: for example, dry rot in sub-floors, failure in roof timbers and water penetration through walls. Skilled survey should obviate most of these items, but cost estimates should always err initially on the side of pessimism.

Once demolition begins, care must be taken not to damage those parts of the fabric which are to be retained. On the other hand, since this is difficult and since time may be important, it is sometimes better to allow for wholesale replacement of certain elements, such as doors, frames, windows and plasterwork, and to accept that the good will go out with the bad. Protection of the building fabric against further degradation is important, whether this be caused by weather or vandalism. Temporary sheeting is needed to protect roof timbers, where tiles and slates have been stripped, windows and door openings must be boarded up and services must be diverted or 'capped'. Finally, the safety of both operatives and intruders must be considered, especially where structural elements are being removed.

In summary:
Survey and measure accurately
Keep occupiers fully informed
Consider re-use of items; when not possible, dispose of and delete any return
    from the contract sum
Allow for concealed decay and degradation
Avoid damaging fabric and fittings which are to be retained
Consider wholesale replacement of certain elements
Protect the fabric against further degradation
Consider safety measures.

(b) Replacing major elements

Major elements which may require substantial restoration or replacement include external masonry, timber, floors and roofs, although sometimes foundations which have settled or which were inadequate to begin with must be underpinned or reinforced.

(i) External fabric: refurbishment here may include the rebuilding or tying together of leaves of masonry which have bowed, settled, separated or otherwise degraded and, usually, the insertions of new dpcs. Care should be taken to decide which measures are the most appropriate: need the wall be demolished and rebuilt, or could tying together with epoxy-coated, stainless steel pins be a satisfactory answer?; has the external wall separated from the party wall? how stable are the old brick chimneys: should they be demolished through the building or capped and retained? When fitting new elements into an existing framed structure, will the new modules fit the old and how will the new components be tied back to the existing ones? Having decided what to do, the work must be organised and carried out deploying the appropriate levels of skill. Since many pieces of work may be sub-contracted, for example the pinning of walls and the insertion of dpcs, guarantees of quality must be obtained and methods of supervision decided.

(ii) Timber floors: in older properties, timber joisted ground floors are often suspect. Their condition can only be decided finally, however, by lifting the floor deck and examining the state of the joists, especially at the points where they are built in to external walls, whether or not there are sleeper walls and if so, whether they meet current statutory requirements, the state of the solum and the condition of any services. Even if the floor is sound, however, it may have to be relaid to meet changes in ground floor layout. It is convenient to list the major points which affect the quality of the work as follows:

Is only partial replacement required? Has a thorough survey of floor condition been carried out?

Will the existing sub-structure be capable of carrying the new floor?

How much will the general fabric of the building be disturbed? Can it be made good afterwards?

Is replacement or treatment of affected timbers and walls a specialist item? Has programming taken account of this?

Will temporary measures have to be taken whilst the floor is being replaced, for example the re-routeing of services?

Have replacement timbers been adequately seasoned and treated against rot?

Are the new timbers and components compatible dimensionally with the old ones?

Has the solum been cleared of rubbish and treated to prevent the growth of organic matter?

Has adequate ventilation been provided for the new floor?

(Check adjacent ground levels to ensure cross-ventilation is possible).

(iii) Roofs: As with all buildings, the roof of the refurbished property must be sound if further degradation of the building fabric is to be avoided. Quality on the job can be badly affected if this stage of the work is carried out during bad weather conditions by poor quality labour and programming of the work may have to be flexible to ensure stripping and replacement only when these factors are not present. Where the weatherproof membranes, tiles, slates, felts, asphalts, only are being replaced, it should be ensured that the roof structure is capable of supporting the weight of operatives working on the roof and that disturbance of the structure does not occur. Often, however, failure in the membranes has been caused by movement in the structure and it is essential, therefore, to correct any deficiencies there before fixing new membranes. Where the structure itself is being renewed, care should be taken to ensure that current statutory requirements are met, especially regarding bearings on wall-plates and party walls, resistance to wind and other imposed loads and resistance to fire. In the case of flat roofs, it is sometimes desirable to replace these with pitched ones, in which case the effects of the new loadings upon walls and foundations must be considered. Finally, attention must be given to flashings, soakers, gutters and downpipes and to the need for thermal insultion in and ventilation of the roof space.

In summary:
Carry out stripping and rebuilding of roofs only during dry weather; ensure good quality labour is used
Ensure existing structure can support new weatherproof membranes
Consider the safety of operatives carrying out this work
Ensure roof structure is sound before replacing membranes
Ensure any new structure meets current requirements for strength, stability, fire and thermal performance
Where replacing a flat roof with a pitched one, ensure new loads can be supported
Ensure exterior plumbing has been completed properly.

(c) Finishes and fittings

As with new buildings, finishes and fittings in refurbished properties are those items which will immediately impress both client and user, yet they are the ones where the temptation to cut corners is the strongest. Unless the underlying fabric is sound, the application of high quality finishes is pointless: paint or paper applied to damp or rotten plaster will simply come off, together with the plaster. New socket outlets connected to old wiring may fail or, worse still, be dangerous. Rotten windows will reject paint as surely as will damp walls. Quality on the modernisation site is very largely to do with attention to the sub-strates, to ensure that surface finishes are sound and not purely, and briefly, cosmetic. Two particular areas call for more detailed comment, plastering and services:

(i) Plastering[2,3] Commonly, especially in refurbished housing, plaster will have degraded. This will be most likely to have happened at the base of ground floor walls, where no dpc was provided, and behind fittings, where wetting may have occurred and ventilation has been poor. It is usual in these circumstances to remove the rotten plaster from the lower part of the wall, install a new dpc where necessary, and to re-plaster. Where this is done, however, particular care must be taken not to break the bond between the sound plaster and the wall behind it and to ensure as far as possible that the wall above the new dpc has dried out. It goes without saying, in the light of the introductory comments above, that the substructure must be sound before plastering takes place, with all structural work completed and any underlying coatings, such as distemper, removed. The correct type and grade of plaster must then be selected taking account of suction and key and with the use of a bonding agent if necessary. Finally, sufficient time must be allowed for drying out if efflorescence is to be avoided and in areas of high humidity it may be necessary to use mould inhibitors and mechanical dryers.

In summary

Consider whether to re-plaster whole walls rather than only the areas where plaster has degraded

Avoid breaking the bond between sound plaster and the substructure

Ensure walls are sound and have largely dried out before re-plastering; remove any old and flaking coatings

Use the correct type and grade of plaster

Take account of suction and key; use a bonding agent if necessary

Allow time for drying out before redecoration.

(ii) Services It is invariably necessary to upgrade the services installations in refurbished buildings. Plumbing services are often inadequate and exposed to frost action, heating other than by open fire is probably non-existent and electrical wiring may have become dangerous over the passage of time and inadequate for the number of socket outlet and lighting points required. During upgrading, in any case, replanning of parts of the building will have taken place, most often affecting sanitary and cooking installations, and this is the opportunity to ensure that new installations are provided, fully up to modern standards. Since the installations are being fitted into an existing fabric, the concealing of pipework, boilers, cylinders, etc, may be difficult. Relatively high quality work may be needed, therefore, to ensure that fittings are mounted square on or against walls and that pipework is neatly laid out. Work is often made more difficult by surfaces not being true and there being limited space for fittings. The same problem of concealment can occur with electrical wiring and outlet points. For this reason, careful planning of wiring routes is necessary and the opportunity should be taken where floors are being replaced or walls replastered to fix new conduit and draw wires. It is often difficult to re-plaster over plaster-depth conduit without showing a ridge and the potential of skirtings for concealing wiring and providing a secure fixing for pipework should be considered. Other points requiring attention include the forming of holes through walls, floors and ceilings, which will require making good later, and mountings for radiators and boilers. The latter in particular will require the connection of a fuel supply and a flue, whose location may be difficult given limited wall area. Finally, any existing flues must be blocked up and ventilated, unless they are to remain in use.

Summary of points

Replan the building taking the services installations into account from the earliest stages

Consider complete replacement, even if some of the existing services could be retained

Consider the problems of concealment of pipe runs and wiring; plan routes
carefully
Allow for surfaces not being true and there being limited space for fittings
Avoid chasing into existing plaster, where possible
Consider how best to form holes in walls, floors and ceilings
Consider fixings and mountings for radiators and boilers
Ensure old flues are blocked up and ventilated.

Conclusion

A high proportion of the workload of the building industry today is concerned
with modernisation or refurbishment. Standards of work on site must be no
less high than with new building, although methods of working may vary and
the organisation of the work-force may have to be different, owing to the
intricacy of much of the work and its non trade-specific nature. Successful
modernisation calls for closely interdependent working between designer and
contractor, with a major contribution from the cost consultant. Objectives
must be clearly identified, cost targets set, surveys meticulously carried out
and the various stages of work clearly organised. Flexibility by all members of
the team is of the essence, since, as demolition proceeds, unforeseen
problems may arise calling for a change of plan. Work must then proceed
ensuring that the basic structure of the building is consolidated before finishes
are applied. Above all, clients expect that their upgraded building will meet
modern standards in all respects; to achieve these within an obsolete fabric
requires team work of a high order.

References
[1]Levitt Bernstein Associates, *Supervisor's Guide to Rehabilitation and Conversion*,
Architectural Press
[2]British Gypsum, *British Gypsum White Book*, 5th edition, British Gypsum 1984
[3]BRE, *Choosing specifications for plastering*, Digest 213, HMSO

10 Conclusion

We have tried in this book to show that the achievement of quality on site and at the work-place can result only from a team effort and from attention to detail at every stage of the building operation. The point has been made that concern for quality must begin from the very inception of the project, from the appointment of the consultants and the drawing up of the brief, and that at this early stage clear agreements about quality levels must be reached between the building owner, the designer and, as soon as possible, the builder. Once agreement has been reached, it must be interpreted by the designer in terms of the purpose, appearance, experience and technical performance which the owner wishes the building to achieve, constrained at every stage by time and cost.

There is little point, however, in the designer producing a design which meets these objectives only on paper. The design intentions must be passed down the communications hierarchy to the builder in his office and on from him to the site, where they must be translated into building by the operatives, working under the direction of their supervisors. Much can be lost during this transfer of information and it is important to use documentation appropriate for each stage of the process and for those who, at each stage, have to make use of it. This requires the selection of managers, supervisors and operatives capable of understanding and applying the information at the agreed quality levels.

Once the decision is taken to build and work starts on site, many aspects of the work, which make a direct impact upon quality, can be overlooked. These include the correct method of establishing the site, of setting out the work and of forming good relationships between all those who will be working together, especially the builder's site manager, the Clerk of Works if appointed and the sub-contractors. As work proceeds from sub-structures through to the finishing trades and to the handing over of the building to the new owner, care must be taken to handle and store materials and components carefully, to prepare them properly for use and to add them to the growing building at the quality level which has been agreed by all parties as being appropriate for that particular job.

Many parts of the job are related critically to the constraints of time and cost and the effects of these have been discussed in some detail. Both parameters have two main elements: effect during the construction process and effect over the life of the building. There is little point in building quickly unless the returns from a rapid completion justify the risks which may have been taken to achieve it. Equally, untried building techniques may result in high costs during the building's life, acceptable only if the owner can justify these in terms of others of his objectives, or if they have been properly discounted during his calculations of building performance.

The last section of the book is concerned with quality and modernisation. Here it is shown that many of the same points apply as for new building, the main difference being in the effects upon the building's occupants, who may have to be moved whilst work is in progress, and upon the existing fabric, large parts of which may be retained. Decisions must be taken which, once again, balance the desirable end of as nearly new a building as possible against the constraints of management, operatives' skills, time and cost.

In conclusion, it should be emphasised that quality in building and especially on site can be achieved only through meticulous planning by all members of the design and building team working together from the earliest possible stage in the project. There is no scope for the taking of professional and sectional stands: the manager of a job should be the person best fitted for that role, regardless of status or title, and all members must be prepared to subsume their professional attitudes and expectations to achieve the agreed end. After all, it is the owner's building and it is he who is paying all who assist him to realise it. We would go so far as to suggest that, unless the established professions and organisations accept this cardinal point, they will risk being replaced by new professions and organisations more flexible in outlook than they and better adapted to the realities of life in the last decade of the twentieth century.

Appendix 1
Assessing quality levels

Chapter 2 referred to the measurement of quality levels in terms of amount and type. This Appendix describes two methods of doing this, the first a quick 'rule of thumb' guide, the second more detailed.

Method 'A'

For any particular building or building type, it is possible to allocate a rating to a number of significant factors in the construction, use and maintenance of the building. Such a rating might be on a scale from 1–10 or 1–100. Any number of factors can be used, the greater the number the better the discrimination.

Example

Consider three types of dwelling: a *system built* type for a local authority of low initial cost and in an inner urban area; a *speculatively built* type for sale in a typical suburb; an *individually designed* type in an outer suburb or rural area. For each type, subjective assessments can be made for a number of factors which, when aggregated, can give some guidance on the quality levels likely to be achieved and therefore where attempts to improve quality ought to be directed. *Table A.A.1* illustrates how this can work. It will be seen that, although there may be disagreement about individual ratings, overall a clear picture emerges of satisfaction with the traditionally designed and constructed private houses and dissatisfaction with the system-built dwelling. With the latter, particular attention should be paid to improving the ease of construction, the status of the dwelling and its location and to making it easier to maintain, given the limited funds available for this purpose. The only real complaint about the private dwellings is rate of construction, compared with the system-built type. Clearly, this method is crude and depends upon assessment by an experienced and disinterested person, but sometimes such quick evaluations are useful.

Method 'B'

The criteria described in chapter 1, in particular functional performance (financial and technical), appearance and experience, can be used to quantify quality assessments in a more systematic and detailed manner than that described in Method 'A'.

Initially, subjective assessments of required quality levels under the above headings must be made. *Diagrams A.B.1* and *A.B.2* give examples of ranges of assessments for different categories of building, which can be as general or as detailed as required by the user. It is accepted that the extremes of these

Table A.A.1

Rating:
1 : Poor
10 : Excellent

	Individually Designed and Built	Speculative Development	L.A. Dwelling System Built
Low initial costs			
(a) Simple form	8	8	2
(b) Well understood construction	7	9	1
(c) Rapid construction	4	5	8
(d) Good buildability	7	7	7
AV:	6.5	7.25	4.5
Low life cycle costs			
(a) Simple form	8	8	2
(b) Well understood construction	9	9	1
(c) Durable materials	9	7	2
(d) Easy maintenance	9	8	2
AV:	8.75	8	1.75

Good appearance

(a) Satisfies expectations as to what a 'house' should be	3	8	9
(b) Provides a good base for furnishings and fittings	3	8	9
(c) Looks well in the landscape	3	7	9
(d) Good status: meets symbolic and cultural norms	1	8	9
AV:	2.5	7.75	9

Good experience

(a) Convenient to use	5	8	9
(b) Well integrated with the community	7	8	7
(c) Close to facilities (shops, schools, etc)	7	7	6
(d) Secure	3	8	8
(e) Good location (relative to occupier's expectations)	1	8	8
AV:	4.5	7.8	7.8
Overall average:	3.3	7.7	7.9

163

ranges are arbitrary, but the middle ranges should be broadly agreed as being realistic by most clients and designers. In the diagrams, each category is allocated a quality range on a scale from 1–100. Although assessments of the appearance and experience which a building should offer will be matters of subjective judgement, financial and technical assessments can be more precisely quantified. Thus, with respect to appearance and experience, the rating scales must be examined by the client and the designer and a decision taken as to where on a particular scale their building should fall. To evaluate the technical quality level, on the other hand, data from available guidelines on materials and components costs should be sought to reach informed decisions. Finally, financial quality should be assessed partly by deriving 'bracketed' ranges from building cost source-books and partly by breaking the building down into cost critical elements, which can then be used to derive an elementary cost plan.

Chapter 7 discussed the two main elements of building cost, initial and life cycle, and how quality levels under each heading could be considered. Again, it would be possible to quantify roughly the relationship between building life and quality levels, enabling clients to make allowances in their maintenance budgets for replacement of shorter life items.

Example

Consider a three-bedroomed detached house, with a floor area of 90 m^2, built in an outer urban area. Taking the subjective elements first, 'appearance' must be decided by selecting a point on the range for domestic buildings shown in *diagram A.B.1*. It is reasonable to assume a fairly high rating for a house of this type, say '60' on a range running from '30' to '70'. 'Experience' must rate equally highly and it would be fair to select a figure of '80' in a range running from '50' to '90'. (*diagram A.B.1*). The more objective elements contained within functional performance, the financial and technical ones, can be assessed more precisely, since objective factors can be brought to bear. This may require an examination of the costs of materials and components as well as a clear separation between initial and life cycle costs. Referring to *diagram A.B.2*, it can be seen that the range for technical performance runs from '20' to '75'; given the kind of house being considered, a figure of '50' seems reasonable. Finally, a financial assessment can be made by taking the known range of building costs of dwellings (1984 prices), tabulated in *A.B.3*, and applying an assessment factor derived from *A.B.2*. Thus, for the house in question, a reasonable point on the range from '15' to '65' would be '60' which, when applied as a percentage to a cost range from £250–750/m^2, would yield a cost per square metre of £550. For a house of 90 m^2, therefore the total building cost would be £49,500. This figure can then be apportioned between building elements, using as a guide any reputable source-book on building costs.

Having completed the above assessments under their different headings, a further table can be constructed, *Table A.B.4*, showing how cost might be apportioned between the different building elements and how assessments

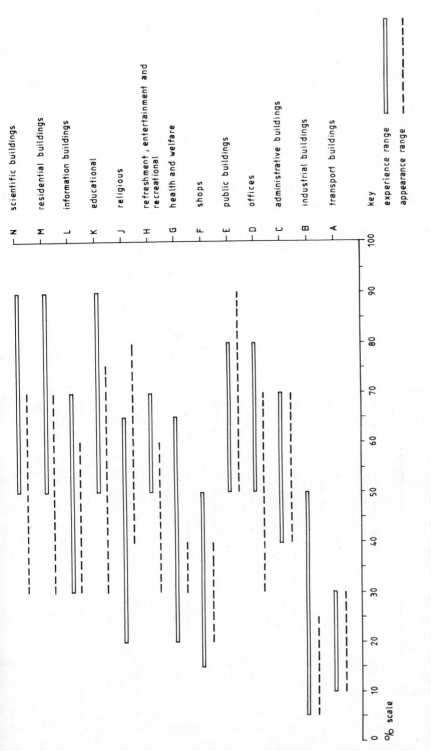

Diagram A.B.2 *Financial and technical performance*

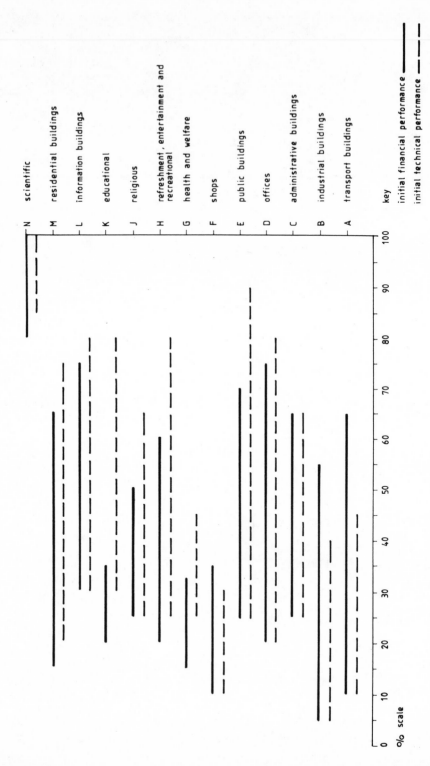

Diagram A.B.1 *Appearance and experience ranges*

BUILDING COSTS ($£/m^2$ floor area)

Scientific buildings	£1400 – £1750/m^2
Residential buildings	£ 250 – £1150/m^2
(Domestic buildings	*£ 250 – £ 750/m^2)*
Information buildings	£ 525 – £1300/m^2
Educational buildings	£ 350 – £ 650/m^2
Religious buildings	£ 450 – £ 900/m^2
Refreshment, entertainment and	
recreational buildings	£ 350 – £1100/m^2
Health and welfare	£ 250 – £ 750/m^2
Shops	£ 200 – £ 600/m^2
Public buildings	£ 450 – £1300/m^2
Offices	£ 350 – £1300/m^2
Administrative buildings	£ 450 – £1200/m^2
Industrial buildings	£ 100 – £1000/m^2
Transport buildings	£ 175 – £1200/m^2

Source: Construction Industry figures

Diagram A.B.3   *Building costs*

under the four headings of appearance, experience, technical and financial performance could be modulated between elements. In many ways this is similar to the construction of a conventional cost plan, with the refinement of weighting each element against a number of factors not usually considered when preparing such plans.

Referring then to *Table A.B.4*, the first two numerical columns show the total building cost of £49,500 apportioned between a range of building elements. The next four columns give assessments under the four 'quality' headings for each element. It will be noted that, where no assessment can sensibly be made, it is excluded and that assessments are weighted to correspond with the perceived need, as agreed between client and designer, of the importance of each element in the building. Totalling and averaging the assessments in each column should match the assessment already agreed for each quality factor, given in the Table at the head of the columns.

The final column in the Table shows estimates of cost for replacement of those elements whose lifetimes are likely to be shorter than that of the building as a whole. Deciding these costs requires a judgement of how long each element will last, that is how many times during the building's life it will have to be replaced, and the likely cost of replacement, including the item itself, of any attendant building work and of labour and plant needed. Rough calculations based on the present example of the house suggests that 20% of the initial cost should be allowed for replacement, apportioned between the elements affected.

Having completed the Table, and having compared assessments against the target assessments agreed for each quality factor, comparison should then be

Area of building	Planned overall cost breakdown		Experience rating 80	Appearance rating 60	Technical rating 50	Financial rating 60	Life cycle rating 20
	£	%					£
Substructures	4500	9	–	–	40	50	
Upper floors	750	1.5	70	40	50	50	
Roof	3500	7	–	50	50	50	
Stairs	500	1	75	60	50	50	
External walls	7500	15	70	60	50	60	
Windows and exterior doors	7000	14	90	60	60	60	5000
Interior walls and partitions	3500	7	90	50	50	70	
Fittings and finishes	6000	12	80	60	–	70	1500
Sanitary goods	1500	3	80	60	40	60	1000
Water services	1900	4	85	60	40	60	
Heating installations	2500	5	85	–	40	60	1500
Electrical services	1250	2.75	85	–	40	60	1000
Gas services	100	0.25	80	–	50	60	
Sideworks	2000	4	80	50	50	60	
Drainage	1500	3	–	–	–	60	
Additional items and contingencies	5500	11.5	80	50	50	60	
Average rating	49,500		80	53	47	59	10,000

Diagram A.B.4 Summary of factors affecting quality assessment

Note: 1984 prices

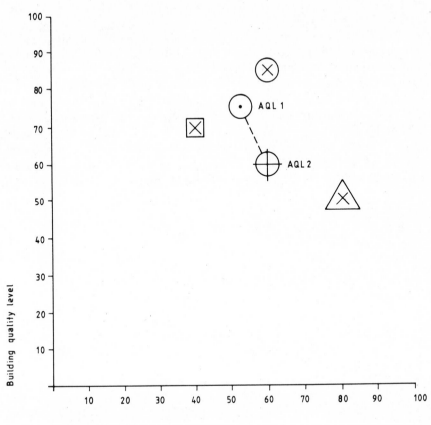

Cost assessment
(sq metre rate expressed on a scale of 0–100)
see diagram A.B.2 : 'Financial performance'

key

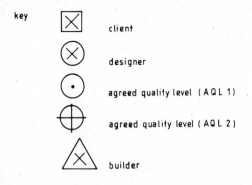

client

designer

agreed quality level (AQL 1)

agreed quality level (AQL 2)

builder

Diagram A.B.5   *Target quality levels*

made between these assessments and the quality level fixed for the whole building. This can be derived most easily by quantifying the Agreed Quality Level illustrated in chapter 2 (*diagram 2.01*). The modified *diagram A.B.5* shows both 'x' and 'y' axes scaled from 1–100, enabling AQL 1 and 2 to be rated as balances between quality and cost. The cost factor has already been agreed as '60' (*diagram A.B.2*) and, as a result of negotiations between client, designer and builder, a quality level of '60' has been fixed for the building: does this '60/60' rating compare satisfactorily with the assessments derived from the detailed analysis? From *Diagram A.B.4* it can be calculated that the overall assessments for experience, appearance and technical performance average '63' and that the financial assessment is in any case '60'. Provided the building is built to these assessment levels, therefore, it will meet its quality targets.

Bibliography

Allen, A H, *An Introduction to Prestressed Concrete*, C & CA, 1978

Austin, C K, *Site Carpentry*, Northwood, 1979

Blackledge, G F, *Man on the Job leaflets* : Nos 1–18, Cement & Concrete Association

BRE, *Quality in Traditional Housing* : Vol. 2 – an aid to design, HMSO, 1982

Davies, William, *Building Plant and Equipment Sheets*, Series 1 and 2, Northwood, 1978

Pilcher, R, *Principles of Construction Management* (2nd edition), McGraw-Hill, 1976

Saint, Andrew, *The Image of the Architect*, Yale UP, 1983

Taylor, J B, *Plastering*, Godwin, 1980

Watts, J W, *The Supervision of Construction*, Mitchell/Batsford, 1980

Weddle, A E, *Landscape Techniques*, Heinemann, 1979

Index